Bottled Dreams

by

Monette Goetinck

Published by Abbott/Adele Books

BOTTLED DREAMS

For permission requests, write to:

ABBOTT/ADELE BOOKS
P.O. BOX 10281
NAPA, CA 94581
Phone: 707-265-8320
email: cspillar@napanet.net

Printed in the United States of America

10 9 8 7 6 5 4 3 2 1

ISBN 0-9669267-1-4
Library of Congress Catalog Card Number 98-89721

Cover Design by April Greiman & Kevin Bosman
of Greimanski Labs
Cover Painting by Roberta Kritzia

*"In my earnest desire to impart
my undying love, I dedicate this book
to Jean-Pierre, my silent son."*

Monette Goetinck

Acknowledgments

Special appreciation is given to all who have helped me to complete this manuscript. I never claimed any authority, although, interspersed with periods of struggle, writing in English is a struggle I do enjoy. Thanks to my devoted husband Jacques whose unparalleled genius always hit right on my computer errors of punctuation and presentation.

My deepest appreciation goes to Joan Davis, my longtime friend and editor, I owe a deep debt of gratitude for turning my French into English, and making creative, imaginative, and actuality, merge together and to Charles Spillar, my dear friend and publisher, my sincere thanks for his unending patience and understanding for finally bringing this book to realization.

My deep gratitude to April Greiman and Kevin Bosman, for having reconstructed the book's jacket so many times and for their courteous help and advice and to Roberta Kritzia for the original artwork for the book's cover.

Special thanks also to the many war brides from Oran, Casablanca, and Algiers, I have met through the years, who offered and shared their knowledge with me and to Suzy Elkins and all my friends and yoga students, for their long support and encouragements, a million thanks.

And, not to be forgotten, thanks to my sweet cat Petit, status symbol of calm as she lay on my papers. She too made her contribution as I recognize how essential we are to each other, for very few could have taught me such inner concentration, and I love her for it.

— M.G.

Table of Contents

Chapter 1 ....*1*

Chapter 2 ....*17*

Chapter 3 ....*35*

Chapter 4 ....*51*

Chapter 5 ....*71*

Chapter 6 ....*89*

Chapter 7 ....*109*

Chapter 8 ....*139*

Chapter 9 ....*171*

Chapter 10 ....*191*

Epilogue *214*

About the Author

Monette Goetinck was born in Algeria in 1914, when it was still a French colony. As her mother died at birth and her father held as a prisoner of war in Germany, she was raised by a rich English uncle who was one of the countless children sired out of wedlock by King Edward VII of England. He owned wineries in Africa and tea estates in India's Assam valley.

Through out her life she writes as a passion and has developed a very strong discipline to this day. Goetinck has written over 8 books, countless books of poetry, short stories, several children's books and a stage play. Whereas many of her poetry books and short stories have been published, *Bottled Dreams* is her first published book. Many others are sure to follow.

Her marriage at sixteen to a French man in Algiers later ended in divorce and produced one son Jean-Pierre. Shortly after World War II ended, she married an American soldier and emigrated to America, being forced by Algerian law to leave her only son behind. Because of her poor financial condition, it was 14 long years before she was to see him again. This marriage too ended in divorce.

To ease the pain of the separation from her son, she began writing daily and teaching yoga. She has now been teaching yoga in Southern California for over 50 years and some of her more famous students have included Marilyn Monroe, Gloria Swanson, Robert Ryan, Ruth St. Denis, and Susan Ball. Her school, Monette's School of Yoga, has been the subject of many published articles about yoga.

Monette Goetinck draws on a vast well of personal experiences for her manuscripts and has developed the writing skills to evoke passion and soul in her work. At the young age of 85, she continues to write daily, teach yoga to a full schedule of students of all ages and lives happily with her husband Jacques and her cat Petit.

Note: Out of respect to the women in this book who suffered tragedies, a few names have been changed and circumstances altered by the author to protect their identity.

INTRODUCTION

In this book I have tried to put into words, like a well prepared meal, the feelings and pain endured by some of the World War II war brides. I was one of them. I only wish I could have written a book filled with joy and happiness, but this was not my case. Do not be stressed by its content and if you find some flaw in the narrative, it will not offend me. We all knew we were taking myriads of chances by marrying complete strangers, yet we were ready to face the fiats of destiny.

The war is easily overlooked as the most discordant notes harmonize again. All is idealized in time of war. We were continuously being surprised at discovering the brave young American warriors with their friendliness, healthy aliveness, and unending generosity. They were good guys, easy to like, easy to fall in love with.

I could have cited many other examples having to do, not specifically with American war brides, like G.I.s married to Japanese girls. Do not believe that we were all uniformly unsuccessful. To the contrary, although we all thought we had picked the best of stars, some of us did not, but many others did and they were the majority. Lucky or unlucky we all have found a treasure isle in America. How could it be otherwise?

As time went by, I learned to like Americans even more, and I finally came to understand that the United States had to become my country. I am proud to be an American citizen and believe that destiny picked me to that end.

This is my story and I told it as it happened. I admit that sometimes my mind has turned instinctively and I have given my own imagination the freedom to soar…and, God, did I soar! It has been many long years and the characters have become mere shadows.

The unpleasant images that infested my mind have faded forever. Unafraid and much stronger, I sprang to life, free to embark on roads leading me to just rewards.

Monette Goetinck

CHAPTER 1

THE YEAR was 1946 and the war at last had ended. It was just about sunset, a delicate pink glow reflected from the sky onto the oil-slicked water. The liberty ship, *U.S.S. Bald Eagle*, her rust-streaked sides looming over the people on the quay, was moored at the little port of Bougie near Algiers on the North African coast. Her irritated captain paced the bridge, casting a jaundiced eye at the Arabs, who, for two days, had been watching the ship's hold fill with cork, coal, and crates of fresh fruit and vegetables. His sailing had been postponed because part of his cargo had arrived only that morning and was just now being loaded aboard.

He was not impressed by the scenery, having seen it all before, and would have preferred the familiarity of the oil refineries of New Jersey. But this was not the reason for his ill temper — delays were to be expected in this part of the world. What really worried him and brought a frosty glint to his eye was the most important part of his lading: the six women clustered in a group on the deck below him who gazed forlornly over the rail at the land they were leaving. Each in her own way was saying a silent goodbye to the life she had known and tried valiantly to conceal her fears from her companions.

There were still faint remnants of ancient grandeur in the ever-watching crowd, and the bright eyes of the always half-starved children followed with longing the movements of those fortunate ones who would soon sail away to the golden lands where no one was ever hungry. The captain glared at the women with complete distaste. They were the French war brides of servicemen of the United States Armed Forces about to join their husbands in America. One of them was the wife of a colonel, for chrissakes. At least another one had to leave her child behind and that would mean no kids underfoot, thank God. The captain's experience had been that all army brass in general were people who knew nothing of sailing and were prone to delight in issuing directives even to those ships' masters who were not under their command. The orders were usually impossible, or mildly insane, or both. He had not, he was grateful, ever had to command a passenger vessel, but he had heard enough stories to regard women on shipboard with deep suspicion. The sea seemed to have an aphrodisiac effect on even the best; he was concerned for trouble among his crew which had been deprived of female company for a long time. If good, wholesome American women were capable of crew destruction, what could he expect of these French females who had been thrust upon him? Everyone knew what French women were like. His job was to deliver them to the United States in good condition, like any other cargo, and he was determined that nothing would foil this plan, but he was still troubled with misgivings.

Well, he had done his best. He had issued strict orders that there was to be no fraternizing between passengers and crew and, to make his orders stick, had quartered the women in the depths of the lowest deck, above the propeller in a secluded section of the ship, away from the men. No one, officers or crew, was permitted on their deck except on his direct orders and the women were not allowed to stray from their aft deck, except to take their meals in the officers' mess where they would eat at their own table on the opposite side far away from the men.

I was one of those six brides, and for me the saddest realization was never being able to see my little boy, with his honey-colored eyes, curly blond hair, from his father's side, not my dark gypsy locks, what would I do? Up until the last minute I hoped he would be able to come with me, but his father took advantage of a French law that gave him unlimited control and he would not permit Jean-Pierre to leave the country.

When I kissed him goodbye before I sailed, I couldn't be sure that we would ever see each other again in this lifetime. His eye was still black from his latest misadventure, a fight with a roughneck at school; it endeared him to my heart even more.

The American consul had given three of us the same rendezvous point where a taxi would bring us to the pier at Bougie. Glancing over now to those two other girls, I wondered if their final parting had been as sad as mine.

Marie, the plainer of the two, had gasped in shock when I told her that he was my son.

"I could never, ever, leave my child," she said. That hurt. Later I would explain why, but this taxi ride was not the time nor place. Marie was plump, a bit matronly, a black French beret topping an old-fashioned navy serge dress; a large gold cross on a chain showed through the sweetheart neckline and matched the thin gold frames of her spectacles through which she peered. Her outburst, I was to find, was uncharacteristic of her, as she turned out to be very shy.

The other girl in the taxi was Arlette, Marie's complete opposite. She introduced herself to us with ladylike manners; I could tell she was an educated girl, somewhat aloof, but perhaps also shy in her own way. She was chicly dressed in the latest fashion, a smart gray suit, suede shoes to match, her elegant long legs crossed, she must have been under the impression she was on her way to sail on a luxury liner.

They both eyed my navy blue pants without a word. My seamstress had run up some narrow-legged cuffed trousers that Greta Garbo had worn in a magazine photo. No female had ever sported men's style pants before in Algiers, and I couldn't be sure of their reception. Whatever it was, I didn't care, I wanted to be comfortable at sea, and was prepared with a pale blue turtleneck sweater to keep out the drafts. Perhaps it fitted a little too tightly over my generous bosom, but I felt good, and knew I looked good in my new outfit. Small, tanned very brown, dark hair in a low chignon, I was tailored, but appropriately dressed, even to my gold loop earrings.

Wrapped in our own thoughts, silently, we stood at the rail. I was sure that we all felt the same, that, no matter how desirable the future, some part of our heart would always remain in the land of our birth. It had been a little easier, earlier in the day, when some of the other girls' parents and families had all come to bid them goodbye, and wish them bon voyage. But now, with the long protracted wait for the cargo, they had all gone, taking their tears and their laughter with them, and we were left in a sort of limbo, our farewells already said but our voyage not yet begun. I, for one, realized once again that I had cast my lot with strangers both on this voyage and at my destination.

My thoughts turned to my new American staff sergeant husband. My handsome Bill, muscular and virile, who had told me so many stories about his gymnasium in Hollywood, and the lovely area where my new home to be was located. He had held me tightly against his broad chest with his strong arms, assuring me in his manly voice that I would be loved by everyone and would have no difficulty in making myself feel right at home. He had confessed that he was never cut out for the military life and indeed would not have been in the Army at all except that he was drafted to teach the other enlisted men how to be physically fit and strong.

"Well, it looks like we're all in the same boat," I commented aloud, not thinking of my unintentional pun. The others turned to me and, bravely, I stuck my hand out to the nearest and said, "I'm Manola, and here is Marie and Arlette."

"I'm Emma," she murmured, not meeting my eyes. I took in that her dark green dress was several sizes too large and far too old for her. Arlette barely deigned to nod, but Marie hastened to clasp her hand, probably recognizing a kindred soul. She was as plain as Marie, but not as plump, also lots of long wavy black hair, bad complexion, and, I'm sure the same thought crossed the other girls' minds as well — how in heaven's name did such an unattractive girl land an American husband?

"And I'm Lola," announced the big one in a loud voice, shaking hands all around. She turned her back completely on the last member of this brave little band, demanding, "When are we going to leave, for God's sake?" She was a lot older than the rest of us, who ranged from about nineteen to around thirty. She was tall and well built, with a mass of brown hair accentuating the clear pallor of her skin. She was dressed as if for a cocktail party, a black silk dressy dress, not at all suitable for a voyage like this one. Her voice reminded me of a lion, alternately panting and roaring and, once she started talking, she seemed unable to stop.

"And who are you?" She turned to the sixth and last of us and bore down on little Gisèle, who, as the youngest, was also the shyest. She was clutching the rail as tightly as she could and probably could not have shaken hands if she wanted to. Small, blue-eyed with a cloud of frizzy blond hair, she was appealing in the way some young women have of eliciting pity for what reason no one knows. She was delicate as glass and appeared as breakable. She mumbled her name and a few words and my ear picked up her somewhat foreign sounding accent.

"Where are you from?" I asked.

"Belgium," she replied, startled. "Could you tell?"

"I have a musical ear," I replied.

"I'm an orphan, and all alone in the world except for my husband," she replied, a little louder than before.

"I'm afraid," lamented Marie, "perhaps I'll never see my father again, he's so old." Her big brown eyes began to overflow with so far unshed tears.

"We're all afraid of something," asserted Arlette not too convincingly, trying to make the girl feel better.

The little group had broken the ice, and between two and then three, we all chatted as if we had known each other for much longer than the few hours we were thrown together.

By now it was dark.

"Can we pull away from the dock in the nighttime?" wondered Emma, her low voice overshadowed by Lola.

"Well of course we can if they ever get a move on, they sail in the dark, just the same as the daytime."

Suddenly there was a commotion at the dock. A taxi had screeched to a halt. Evidently we had long stowed the cargo but were still waiting for the seventh and last passenger.

Here was a scene.

Long dark red hair streaming behind her, camel hair coat tossed matador-style over her shoulders, this young lady showed none of the signs of parting, unhappiness, nor indecision we all felt. Striding forcefully up the gangplank, amidst wolf whistles from the crew, self-assured and quite aware of the effect of her late arrival, she passed the first mate with a drowning glance into his eyes, a fleeting smile guaranteed to make him follow her and relieve her of the sole suitcase she carried. As he set it down next to her, she thanked him in a throaty voice and bestowed upon him an intimate wink.

Lola rubbed her eyes as if not believing what she saw and uttered a loud "whoa".

Suddenly she was among us, shaking hands like a polished politician, introducing herself with more ease and familiarity than any of the rest of us had shown. Her large doe-shaped eyes were remarkable, they seemed to change from green to brown to hazel flecked with gold, all in the matter of an instant. Later I was to find out what she was thinking from the way her eyes changed color, like a chameleon moving from tree branch to leaf.

This was Nadia and, with her arrival, things began to happen. Out of the murk of the night, a white-coated steward emerged to announce the start of dinner in half an hour.

"Please do not be late, the captain does expect everyone to be punctual."

I had slipped into our designated quarters earlier so that I could have a private cry, and in doing so had picked out an upper bunk with a port-hole. This stateroom, in comparison to a passenger liner's, was cramped and squalid. Because it appeared to have been added as an afterthought, this cabin lacked everything except the most basic necessities — space included. Upon stepping up over the hatchway, to the right and left were three tiers of bunks; next to the right side someone had placed a cot, for the seventh passenger. Straight ahead was the bathroom which contained a wash-basin, a toilet and a very narrow stall shower. Everything smelled as if it had been newly painted for us in a yellow-creme. Some thoughtful person had mounted a mirror on the bulkhead with a shelf below it, opposite one side of the hatch to the bath-room. The same thoughtful person had also put up some hooks on each side of the entrance. A number of wire coat hangers were hung on them to give us the idea, if we didn't already guess, what they were for. There was only room for three folding canvas-back chairs. A minuscule shelf, mounted in the cor-ner of the right bulkhead, held a creme-colored enameled clock with a large white face and black

Arabic numbers. Someone had either taken the trouble to match the accessories or perhaps it was just a lucky accident. What would it be like when all of us were in there at the same time, I wondered, what with the smell of humanity and the new paint, it would be unbearable.

I could imagine Arlette's superior sniff when she saw these minimal accommodations. Like me, she had probably traveled with her parents on several well-equipped passenger liners and would find her new home ugly and uncomfortably congested.

When the others entered, complaining about the small space allotted to us, I gave up my place at the mirror and climbed up to my bunk to make room for them.

"Oh, isn't this horrible?" cried one of them, I don't remember which. "Where am I going to hang my clothes?" moaned another. I sat cross-legged on my upper tier berth, brushing my hair, bemused, and watched the little drama unfold.

Suddenly, "Ooh-la-la, and whom do you think you're going to catch with this?" challenged Lola, reaching for my bottle of Chanel and liberally sprinkling me with it. "Of course Madame doesn't know whom she may meet," this with a ribald guffaw to the others who had stopped to listen.

Soberly, I took the bottle away from her. "Just because I'm on this tub doesn't mean I'm going to let my standards down. It has nothing to do with catching or meeting anyone. I caught mine and am looking forward to meeting him in a month's time."

Mockingly Lola did a little bow, "My apologies, *chère Madame*, I didn't mean to be rude, I was just teasing, please forgive me if I offended you."

It was difficult to stay angry at her, but I

noticed that her accent which had started out a fair French soon lapsed into a sort of mixture of French, Spanish and Arabic just like the slang spoken in the lower-class Bab-el-Oued quarter of Algiers.

"Let's be civil to each other; after all, we have a long way to go together and I would rather be friends than not."

She stuck out her big paw and said, "Shake on that."

A knock at the door took us all by surprise. After glancing around, we, as one, chorused, "*entrez!*"

The captain stood framed in the open hatch-way. Small, heavy, and white-haired, he was probably near the end of his service and this was not a duty he wanted nor asked for. His blue eyes and pink cheeks rather made him look like Father Christmas but there was no twinkle in his stern eyes as he looked each and every one of us straight in the face.

"My French is poor, so I will need some assistance, I assume most of you speak English, but I may need some help in translating what I say, who wants to help me?"

"I will be happy to help, Captain." Arlette's dulcet tones conveyed her elegant English before I could volunteer.

"Please translate this exactly as I say it, girls, this trip is going to be a long and hard one. If we are all to get along together I will tell you that you are not, under any condition, to talk to, flirt with, or have anything to do with any of the men on board. Not officers, nor enlisted men. Is that absolutely clear?"

He waited a moment for Arlette to translate

but I could tell by the expressions on their faces that they understood him in English quite well.

"These are the rules, and I will not stand for anyone to break them. This is the law, if you will, and on this ship, I am the law. Is this understood?"

He drew himself up, and, tight-lipped, asked, "Is there anything you want to ask me?"

I raised my hand. "Captain," I asked innocently, "would you have an iron and an ironing board?"

I might as well have asked him for the moon, a dish of larks, or the Tower of London, to have seen the expressions play over his face. His imagination must have been racing to the picture of the saltier members of his crew, slaving over a hot iron in the galley, pressing their underpants, and he shook himself a little, squared his shoulders and said, without a note of regret, "Sorry, but you'll have to learn to live without them."

Arlette, the colonel's wife, our translator, languidly indicated our surroundings. "This cabin is deplorable, Captain, could you please move me? And also, I would like another pillow, if you don't mind."

Lola jumped in before the captain could reply.

"What, who do you think you are, Missus? What about us? Why should you have a better place or another pillow?"

Arlette toyed with the pearl strand around her neck, grasped the captain's arm, gave it a squeeze and said, "I would so appreciate it, Captain."

We all giggled at Lola's aside, "I wish she'd slip on a banana peel and break that pretentious ass of hers."

Shocked, prudish Marie put her hands over her ears, but luckily the captain didn't understand Lola's peculiar accent very well so the smutty remark went past him.

Suddenly another man appeared in the open doorway. Blond and stocky, his welcoming smile showed perfect white teeth under the little shadow of a pale mustache. Where the captain's blue eyes were cold and piercing, this man's were sparkling and startling in his tanned face. Ringlets of blond hair escaped his uniform cap as he took it off, as if to give the lie to his masculinity which he evidently strove to project. This was our late arrival suitcase-toter that we had seen on the gangplank.

"Meet Mr. White, the first mate. When I'm not available, you can ask him for what you need, but not an iron nor an ironing board." This last with a glare in my direction, as if to warn me to mind my manners.

"We'll have supper shortly and we'll sail directly after. It will be served every evening at six o'clock sharp. Your waiter is Billy and you can ask him for whatever you want to drink between meals during the day. But, do not be late." The two men turned, stepped over the hatchway and left the cabin, followed by Arlette still pleading for another pillow.

Lola shrugged her shoulders. "What guts! And what a peacock she is!"

Marie plaintively remarked, "It's as if she doesn't want any part of us. Why? Does she think we're not as good as she is?"

Triumphantly Arlette returned with her extra pillow and, for a bonus, another blanket. Lola jeered and applauded.

"There is no other cabin to be had, it appears," Arlette complained to no one in particular, while the rest of us ignored her, tested our mattresses, fixed ourselves up as best we could for our first shipboard dinner. Arlette changed her suit for a smart silk frock which, strangely enough, wasn't even wrinkled. She slipped on yet another pair of high heels, and, except for the lack of a hat, looked as if she was going to tea at the Casino.

Nadia, the latest arrival, familiarly proceeded to regale us with an involved account of why she had been late. She pulled a bright dress out of her suitcase, peeled off the red and black jersey one she'd arrived in, wiggled the new one over her head and yanked it down over her shapely hips.

The captain had acknowledged our presence by a curt nod when we filed in to what we thought of as the dining room, and the other officers studiously ignored us following the captain's instructions. Our long trestle table was placed as far away from that of the men as the cramped space allowed and was covered in a well worn red and white plastic checked tablecloth. It reminded me of the little family bistros at home and, for a moment, I felt a pang of homesickness. There was a smudged chrome-topped salt and pepper shaker set with a matching sugar bowl in the center. The silverware was bent and dented and didn't look too clean. Paper napkins, which were still a novelty in our country, were at each place.

"This is a first," commented Arlette aloud.

"Why?" I asked.

"It's the first time I've ever had to eat with such a tablecloth and such horrible looking service."

"You should know," this with a low aside to

me. The others were poking each other with their elbows and giggling at her. She fell into silence, contenting herself with surreptitiously polishing her fork with her paper napkin, replacing it, picking up the knife and spoon in order, to give them the same treatment, a disdainful expression on her face.

Billy, our waiter was a negro, a lovely chestnut brown color, what a difference compared to the pitch black Senegalese at home.

We were happy not to be required to talk, therefore our first meal aboard was a quiet one, we were all preoccupied with our own thoughts and feelings. The food was filling but unremarkable.

When supper was over, we rose from the table and filed out. Not a head turned to watch us.

"Damn it," said Nadia breathlessly, "let's go have a last look at our country from the deck, eh?"

Without waiting for agreement, she pulled the arm of the nearest girl, slope-shouldered little Gisèle, who, like a shrimp peering from under a rock, allowed this confident stranger to sweep her up in the tidal wave of her energy.

"What's your name, honey?" asked Nadia in her rich, strong voice. "Tell me your name again?"

Mesmerized, frozen Gisèle answered in a whisper. Emma tagged along beside them.

I reached the deck, they were a pretty sight, Nadia in the middle, with arms thrown protectively across Gisèle's and Emma's shoulders, as if even she somehow found comfort in being close to another. We all gathered in a cluster again, except for Arlette, who had picked a spot away from the rest of us to emphasize that, while she was with us, she was not one of us.

There we watched the crew, busy about their

duties. We could feel the throb of the engines beneath our feet, and hear the clang of bells, as the strip of water between us and the land widened, slowly at first, and then faster and faster, and finally disappeared.

As if hypnotized, Marie, in a monotone voice, eyes filling with tears said, "I just can't face the idea of never seeing my parents again, I'm their only child. My dad is getting so old, I will never forget the sight of his poor, tired bent back, plodding up the hill away from the port this afternoon."

Emma added sympathetically, "I feel the same way, at least my brothers will run the farm and my parents won't miss their only daughter too much with that noisy bunch around."

Arlette spoke suddenly, "Well, I'm sure you're both going to enjoy a more glamorous future than what you were used to, so look on the bright side, and know you're going to have it better." We looked at her with a grudging admiration for these kind words.

Our voyage to a new life had begun.

We retreated to the cabin. Our mood was somber and there was little conversation, even Nadia and Lola were subdued. In turn we prepared for bed, undressing in the bathroom.

Arlette emerged at the end of her toilette and all eyes fastened on her. Wrapped in the most expensive heavenly blue silk peignoir, she wafted the scent of Yardley soap and lotion about her and those less fortunate sniffed in appreciation. It made the dampness of the cabin, for just a moment, a bit more bearable. Not even I, with my bottle of Chanel, was as elegantly appointed as she.

"Can we turn the light off now?" In chorus a

half dozen voices responded, "Yes". Lola slipped out and flipped the switch.

After a while, the cabin was so quiet that every creak and groan of the ship could be heard as she cut her way through. We felt the engines and the sound of the water threshed by the propeller grew louder until even they were overridden by a subdued drone which seemed to be very close by.

Moved by a common impulse, we found its source in Marie, on her knees beside her bunk, rosary in hand, dressed in a no-nonsense cotton nightgown which covered her from neck to instep, busily saying her prayers. She went on and on, endlessly. There were restless movements from the other bunks as tensions mounted. Would she ever stop? Like a turtle emerging from its shell, Lola stuck her head out of her bunk and emitted a stentorian Amen.

All eyes focused on Marie as she scrambled guiltily into her bunk. There was a collective sigh of relief and a perceptible feeling of relaxation.

CHAPTER 2

THE *BALD EAGLE* trudged her way west through the Mediterranean, so far skillfully avoiding mines, after all this was post-war, while we delved into each other's past history and explored one another's personalities. All we knew were our names and that every one had an American husband waiting at our destination. Others disclosed personal secrets which under normal circumstances would never see daylight. Confidences, hopes, and desires were shared. We were seven strangers thrown together by fate, probably destined to never meet again after the voyage's end. We found that some had never sailed before and were frightened — afraid of seasickness, drowning, the unknown.

For the first time in our lives we felt free. Free to be honest with ourselves and with others. We were cut off from the life we had known and were experiencing a sort of rebirth in which we could be what we wanted to be — or pretend to be what we wanted to be — responsible only to ourselves and those who shared this voyage.

The captain, in an effort to be cordial, had told us we would be able to see Gibraltar and its famous Rock if we got up before dawn. His offer was met with enthusiasm from those who had never seen it, which was nearly everyone. Unfortunately the toll of leaving, the strangeness of the surroundings and the fact no one had slept well *until* dawn prevented us from sailing through the straits awake.

The morning arrived cold and gray and the wind was whistling around the portholes of our cabin. The motion of the ship had become more violent, and, as we dressed, we were thrown off balance frequently by sudden lurches. I had to grab at the bunk supports or whatever I could reach to keep from stumbling. I kept peering out through the portholes and, to my amazement, wherever I looked, I could see only water, cold gray waves, flecked with whitecaps. A lone sea gull flew by, her tragic cry mingled with surf and wind. I reflected on the many miles we had to go before reaching our destination and our husbands. Already I was missing the long line of cliffs left behind, Algiers the White, the pearl of the Mediterranean. I was leaving my birthplace, the only home I ever knew, my child, for the G.I. I barely knew, and had married.

Looking out, mesmerized, this was not the blue Mediterranean as seen from the African coast, placid and friendly, basking under a hot sun with decorative white clouds sailing slowly overhead. This cold and alien sea was ominous and I shivered in the crisp morning air.

With Nadia and Lola it was impossible to maintain an air of dignified reserve. They were here, there and everywhere — commenting on the appearance of their companions, making smutty remarks, and laughing uproariously at their own jokes. Only Arlette maintained her air of superiority with the others; with me she was natural and pleasant, treating me as an equal. Of course this was because I passed the test of, "Do you know so-and-so?" She played her little game of one-upmanship to the exclusion of all the others, which made me uncomfortable but did not seem to affect them at all.

I was treated to a detailed account of Arlette's social triumphs but it was difficult to reconcile her stories about people my parents had entertained at home for dinner many times and whom my father would have characterized as "silly asses".

At breakfast, we were at our table when the hatch to the galley swung open behind Billy the waiter. We caught a glimpse of a fat cook who was swearing softly to himself as he tried vainly to make toast on some makeshift contraption. The air was blue with smoke from burned bread. It was quite plain that, regardless of the other skills he might have had, toast making was not one of them. The typical American breakfast then, scrambled eggs and nearly burned bacon, made us lament our native sausage, highly spiced and fragrantly delicious. Our breakfast at home was usually at a later hour. Once again, it became apparent that we would not be taking food for granted anymore, everything was going to be new and different. We talked freely. Nadia and Lola made no attempt to conceal their interest in the men at the other table and kept stealing glances at them, poking each other and giggling.

Lola was particularly fascinated by the first mate, Mr. White, who was indeed an eager trencherman and happy to demonstrate it to all who might be interested. He was concentrating on his food which streamed from his plate to his mouth in a continuous flow.

"God, look at him eat," she marveled. "I wonder if he screws with the same enthusiasm," this last with a loud snort and a gesture of "ooh-la-la" with her wrist in admiration.

"He must be really *something*."

This drew a welcoming laugh from Nadia.

"The other one, isn't he the chief engineer? He's not too bad either. I wouldn't throw him out of my bed. Or at least, I wouldn't have before my marriage, but of course, I was never too fussy."

The rest of us buried our faces in our napkins.

Arlette said, "Remember the captain's order about not communicating with the men. I, for one, do not intend to spend this voyage locked up in that tiny cabin, so watch your step."

The wind and cold were too much to endure for most of us accustomed to the hot sun of our homeland. In spite of my desire to exercise, I was too uncomfortable.

"Oh well, I'll miss a day," I thought.

I followed the others back to the cabin where I found them huddled in their bunks. The warmth felt good after the wind, and now we listened to the whistling, the sea roaring against the steel hull of the ship like a conch shell held to the ear.

I was nursing my sorrow this first morning separated from my son, when Lola turned and confronted me.

"Were you ever married before, Manola?"

Roused from my bittersweet reveries, I returned to the present. It embarrassed me to be the center of attention, but I nodded, somehow knowing where this would lead.

I cowered in my bunk hoping this would satisfy my questioner, but the nosy Lola had only begun.

"Tell us, Manola, do you love your American more than your first husband?"

"What a question! One can love a thousand times in life, each time differently."

Nadia stared at me, a beautiful smile framing her lips.

"A thousand, how true."

"And you, Nadia, before G.I. Joe, were *you* married before?"

She lowered her head. "No, my life was somewhat different. You wouldn't have known, any of you, what it was, struggling just to survive. Life is a dangerous game, my friends, and you couldn't know what it's like to flirt with death on a daily basis. I was alone since age fourteen and had a good sampling of what starvation was. Men were the obvious answer to my problem of eating and there was no one to tell me differently. When I met my M.P. I thought I could start over in a country where no one knew me and ...," her voice trailed off.

"Did *he* know about your past?" I inquired.

"Of course not, why buy the cow when you can get the milk for free," she giggled. "His family owns a spread in Texas, whatever that means, so life will certainly be very different. But Rich is so smart, I know he'll make lots of money and then we'll be truly rich!" and she crowed at her little joke.

"Sounds like you're already half-way there," Arlette observed sagely.

Lola broke in, "You're not the only one that had a lover or two before marriage, what an idiot I hooked up with the first time around, skinny and dumb, poorer than me, even. But I was never married before, and, now that I am, nothing is going to stop me from having everything I've always wanted. I'll have a beautiful home and lots of children, you'll see. I never had a home of my own. I was an orphan from birth."

Marie, tender-heartedly voiced a soft "ooh".

"Yes, raised by musty nuns who threw work my way as soon as I was able to handle it: laundry, lots and lots of dirty laundry to wash and iron. I've never known anything else. Not like you or you," derisively sticking her chin out at Arlette and me.

"My legs are ruined from those years of standing, swollen with varicose veins that look like a road map of rural Algiers. But, I'm not complaining, never mind that, thanks to my good washing and ironing I was able to meet my Stefan."

"Is Stefan her husband?" asked Gisèle softly of Marie.

"Yes," Lola answered, "I got to know one particular American serviceman."

Her black eyes flashed and rolled, "If you only knew, girls, how passionately I ironed his shirts," and she moved her arm and body in an ironing motion with a little bump and grind at the end that made us all laugh.

She wasn't through. "I think we're pretty lucky to have married Americans. I hear that, in America, the woman wears the pants. What a switch that will be! To be treated like a queen. European men expect a woman to clean their boots and wait upon their every desire like slaves."

"Oh what do you know about it? That's not always true," protested Emma hotly. All eyes turned to her. This quiet unattractive girl, unused to being the center of attention, spoke out firmly, her cheeks blazing. "My father didn't expect my mother to wait on him. They shared everything equally, except maybe their love for their children. They always loved the boys, my brothers, best. As the only girl, I know I'll be missed on the farm where I worked so hard, but I'll miss the farm even more. It's so beautiful out there, the big trees so green in front of our house, the sky so pure and blue, even when it was dry and desolate, to me it was always beautiful. My Jimmy tells me that wheat is a big crop in Montana and that the land there is very rich, much richer than North Africa will ever be. He's a horseback rider in something called a rodeo, and although I don't know much about what he does exactly, I know it has to be dangerous because his father had an accident doing the same thing and is now paralyzed. I'll be taking care of him as well, because Jimmy's mother is gone now and I'll be in charge. I was raised very poor, but we always had more than enough to eat and, as far as I'm concerned, my husband can wear the pants if he wants to." Her furious blush had illuminated her pimples as it spread to her hairline and her voice died away as if aghast at her temerity in speaking out for so long.

Gisèle took up the thread. "I too am excited and frightened to go to America where everything is so big." Her voice quavered, she was as painfully shy as Marie or Emma.

"I'm Belgian, you know," with a little smile to me, "and our men definitely wear the pants, as you say, but I only know that from hearsay because I was never married before either. I'm an orphan too, and came to Algiers in service to a family related to the one I worked for at home. I met my husband in the garden of their house while everyone was in siesta except me. I loved to have that time alone to relax and dream and, one day, he happened by. His camp was near and he strolled past our garden while I was gathering violets. We started to talk a little, the first time in my poor English and his poorer French, and he returned every day after that. We fell in love, it was our secret and my employers were astounded when I told them I was leaving and the reason. They weren't very happy, but I saw a chance for a new life and a fresh start with someone who, although older than me, is gentle and caring. I don't feel like a maid when I'm with him, he treats me like a queen and makes me happy. He's some kind of a salesman, I don't know what he sells but he travels a lot and we're going to live on the West Coast."

"Oh, where?" I exclaimed. "Anywhere near Beverly Hills, California?"

"I don't know, is that near South Los Angeles," she smiled shyly, and suddenly I realized that at least two of us were headed in the same direction.

"I hope we can be friends in our new life, after all, we'll be neighbors," I responded warmly, there was something so sweet about her.

Arlette stopped brushing her hair long enough to comment. "I hope all you girls were smart enough to get two marriage certificates."

"Why?" we wanted to know.

"Listen to what happened to a friend of mine. She thought she was legally married to her Air Force captain because she had her French certificate. One morning the captain was gone, leaving her a note telling her he was going back to his real family in America, and of course she was out of luck."

"Why?" we all asked again.

"Why, because she wasn't married with an American certificate, so she and her little boy were without any leg to stand on legally. She had no money, he hadn't left her a sou. They had had nearly two happy years together with her living her dream, but it all came to a very sad end."

24

There was a long silence while everyone digested this piece of information.

Lola laughed out loud. "Well, that's it then, if he wants to get rid of me, he can, because I only have a French document, I don't think I have the necessary American one." No one else volunteered to join her in this confession, so I had no way of knowing which, if any, of the others were not strictly legal, but Arlette had brought up a sobering point. How ignorant we all were of both laws, those of the old country as well as the new.

Our idea of America largely came from the movies, that international educator, and, in addition to the Westerns, my new husband Bill had told me already that Hollywood was filled to the brim with beauties, each one more glamorous and sexy than the next; I wondered how we average looking girls could compete and hold onto our husbands against such odds, with goddesses larger than life. I could read the concern on their faces as I shared Bill's information.

None of us had noticed that the pitching and rolling of the ship had increased. The stern, where our cabin was located, dropped like a broken elevator straight down into the trough between two gigantic waves. The ship recovered with a sickening lurch, rose again, only to repeat the performance. Another twisting lurch, incorporating a pronounced side to side slow roll which caused a chorus of terrified squealing females. Lola turned green, shuddered like a racehorse and muttered, "All of a sudden, I don't feel good. I feel as if my gizzard keeps coming up to my throat and I have to swallow to get it to go down again."

She gave an agonized moan and hurried out

the hatch. This caused Marie to clap her hand over her mouth and run behind her. As if that was the signal, both Gisèle and Emma followed, retching violently as they fled.

Nadia sat erect, her face suddenly gone pale, beads of perspiration dotting her upper lip and brow. Wordlessly she pressed her handkerchief to her mouth and also made a hurried exit through the open hatch which the wind banged behind her. Arlette and I looked at each other, shrugged, then turned as Lola, re-entering, cocked a quizzical eye at us and said, "The fishes have had their dinner, girls, and I feel much better."

Perhaps, because both Arlette and I had sailed before, we weren't as frightened nor as disoriented as the others so we were not affected, at least not initially.

It was difficult to eat lunch with the ship's groaning motion and the erratic skittering of the plates around the table. None of us were very hungry anyway, and were a more subdued group than at breakfast.

Billy hovered over us solicitously, noticing we barely picked at our food. When dessert was served he placed in front of each of us a small dish containing a quivering concoction of riotous colors in poison green, strawberry pink, violent orange and electric yellow.

"What is this?" hooted Lola irrepressibly. Really, it was impossible to keep her down long.

"This is called *Jell-O*," Billy solemnly introduced us to our new discovery.

"Pretty shaky," said Lola, wiggling the dish. "This one looks just like the underarm of my neighbor, Mme. Christine."

"I love it!" I exclaimed, smacking my lips.

"You want mine? whispered Gisèle, indicating her almost untouched dish.

"No, no, you try it, go ahead," I urged.

She tentatively tasted it to appease me, but pushed her dish in my direction.

"Here, you like it so much, please eat mine, you like it better than I do."

This generous gesture impelled me to tell her she was sweeter than the *Jell-O* itself.

We giggled, but there was silence as we all quickly polished off our unusual treat.

Suddenly Arlette gasped and we turned to her end of the table. There, busily attempting to help Billy clear away, was Marie, scraping and stacking dishes and silverware just as she used to do at home.

We stared at her and shamefacedly she said, "I always helped wait tables at my parents' cafe. That's where I met my monkey."

Lola snorted.

"I call him that, his real name is Johnny, he's going to have his own dance band someday, he was studying music at the University when the war started. He could have gone to O.C.S. and become an officer but he's a musician at heart and didn't want the responsibility for ordering other men around."

Arlette sneered, but Marie continued, "He used to come alone every day at the same time to sit at one of our little outside tables, stare at our version of the Bois de Boulogne, and drink a coffee or a lemonade. He liked to practice his French on my parents, and I developed such a crush on him, you can't imagine. Because he was always by himself, my father encouraged him to come around by digging out bottles of his vintage liqueurs and wines that he'd never serve to just anyone, and I think he's really responsible for Johnny being interested in me, he kept bringing me over to engage him in conversation. He's so handsome and tall, I could just sit and stare at his face all day and do nothing else." She blushed, her glasses fogging up with suppressed heat and tears.

Nadia smiled, "I bet pretty soon he was practicing his French on you, am I right? Did he get a good grip on his subject?" and she giggled, insinuating something other than what Marie meant.

Before she could answer, Lola grasped the waiter's arm.

"So tell me, where are those big ice creams with all the goo on them that my husband told me about?"

"Tonight," said Billy. "All right? Tonight you'll have your ice cream with all the trimmings, I promise."

"For sure?" insisted Lola.

"For sure," he answered.

The wind seemed to drop somewhat, at least enough for us to breathe a little outside. Either we had developed our sea legs, or the ocean cooperated as we didn't feel queasy and took a little walk up and down. The sun shone at last, and the crew was scattered about the other decks working desultorily at their assigned jobs. Each man was somehow conveniently placed in a position to get the best possible view of us as we paraded under their scrutiny on our private walk.

Their comments on our appearance and probable sexual performance were bawdy and unrestrained, presumably because they thought we couldn't understand them. Nadia garnered the most accolades and appeared to be their first choice. A big bruiser, with bulging muscles, bushy eyebrows and a drooping mustache, spoke for all of them when he raised his head to the sky, inhaled through dilated nostrils as if smelling something delicious and howled, "I could fuck any one of 'em."

Eyes straight ahead, smothering our smiles, we demurely ignored them as we had been bidden.

I desperately wanted to exercise but knew I wouldn't be able to at this time of day. I planned to get up early and claim the deck before anyone could see me, as I knew I would receive a fair share of comments from the seamen.

"Too bad we can't play tennis," commented Arlette.

"Yes, at least I have a racket, didn't you bring yours?" I countered.

"No, my husband said I could buy anything I wanted when I arrived in New York, not to drag too much with me, but I noticed yours, do you play well?"

The other girls stopped to listen.

"If I do say so myself," I replied evenly, "I am pretty damn good." That drew a laugh from everyone.

"My father and I played everyday at home, does your husband play?" I asked.

"I really don't know, we never got into that line of discussion. All I know about Charles is that he looked wonderful in his uniform, that he was introduced by some very important people we knew and that his family owns one of the biggest department stores in New York City."

Game, set, match.

After the cold and dreary beginning, the ones who had been sick wanted to recuperate in the warmth of the sun's healing rays.

"I wonder if we can get some deck chairs from the nice first mate," I thought aloud.

"You can't ask for anything, Arlette should do it, she's better at asking and getting than any of us," said Marie.

We sent Arlette and continued to walk, back and forth, up and down, and when she returned with the captain's comment that, "This is not a luxury cruise," we decided to sit, as we were, on what God had given us, propped up against the ship's bulkhead, legs outstretched, staring out to sea, like crows in a row on a telegraph wire. This soon made our bottoms sore, so we resumed our aimless strolling up and down, and, before long, I knew I would not want to spend the entire voyage in this manner.

The sun slowly sank and the gentle breeze picked up an edge. Shivering, one by one and two by two, we returned to the warmth of the cabin to preen and primp, renew lipstick, comb hair, and fix up for dinner and the promised ice cream.

Relaxed after a calming day in the sun, and, despite the earlier seasickness of the others, everyone was hungry enough to overlook the fat cook's deficiencies and have a hearty appetite. Little by little our ease with each other and our surroundings grew, and, instead of leaving as soon as we were finished eating, we tucked into the giant ice creams with zeal, then clustered together at one end of the table to leisurely drink our coffee and pick up our confidences where we left off.

"Well, my Stefan was right about one thing so

far, at least," commented Lola, stirring her coffee energetically.

"What?" I asked. I seemed to be the one the others turned to for comment and clarification.

"The food is not much compared to ours, but they do know how to do dessert at least," and she gave me a poke in the ribs with a satisfied wink.

Lola was not afraid. A perennial optimist, filled with boundless energy that led to confidence in her ability to take care of herself as she always had. She saw her new future unfold as an adventure to be tested, savored, and swallowed, just like the ice cream. She bolstered the spirits of the more timid girls and was generous in her dealings with the others. In spite of myself I liked her bawdiness even though I found it embarrassing.

"And what does your Stefan do?" I found myself asking her.

"He builds things with some big construction company in Baltimore, where the ship lands. At least we don't have to go so far to be together when he meets me at the dock", and she poked me again, even more vigorously with a lewd wink.

We talked a lot those first few days about everything, private topics, even sex was included. We went round and round on the same subject, how to hold onto our husbands in a country where every woman looked like a movie star.

"But we're French," boasted Lola beating her chest like a silverback gorilla, while we laughed.

After a stop in the cabin for warmer clothes, we took a turn or two on the deck. I was happy for my white coat, made out of a U.S.A. blanket which my clever dressmaker had lined in a red and white print. It was heavy, thank heavens, the others didn't have anything quite as warm. Marie put on an unflattering brown coat, too big and too old for her, but at least it kept the chill out — the other girls had only sweaters which they layered one over the other. Arlette's long wool jacket from yet another of her suits served her well. I imagined her colonel buying her a fur coat when she arrived. No one had known how cold the nights would be.

In spite of my coat, I was still the first back into the cabin, but I had an ulterior motive. I wanted to have the first shower and stripped off my clothes before the others got there. I caroled and splashed with gay abandon, but, afraid of using up all the hot water, cut my bathing short when they began to bang on the door.

I was freezing, but, wrapped in my towel I jumped up the ladder into my bunk where I shrugged into a nightgown and huddled under the blanket.

"We need a bailing pot in here," complained Marie. "Just look at the water all over the floor, the drains must not work very well, or else you didn't close the curtain behind you."

I called out my apologies and offered to mop up the floor, with what I had no idea.

The drain eventually worked, albeit slowly, and as they waited, one by one they disrobed and took turns at shouting good-naturedly who was going after Marie, the next bather. I observed their character traits unfold, and had a few surprises. Most just wrapped their towels around their waists and sat on their bunks waiting, except for Emma who clothed herself in what looked like an oversized pair of a man's long boxer shorts with white lace ruffles. They were the type of drawers my grandmother would have worn in the country years ago, modest enough to cover her from waist to knee. She was elected next and held her towel close to her bosom to conceal it. When she caught my eye and my grinning face, she blushed.

Nadia laughed out loud. "So, do you plan to take your shower in your pants, or what?"

As soon as Marie emerged, Emma dove through the door like a rabbit returning to its burrow.

When Emma came out, dressed in her nightgown, all signs of the embarrassing underdrawers gone, Nadia stretched like a lazy cat, swung her feet to the floor, and her towel fell off. Oblivious to her nudity, she bent to pick it up and drape it about her robust neck. She flaunted her nakedness like a flag, and Marie's prudish jaw dropped in shock at the sight.

Following Nadia's bold example, shy Gisèle also stripped. Her body was a uniform pale amber without mark or blemish, undeveloped like an adolescent boy. Both Lola and Arlette decided to wait until morning since the line was too long.

One day wound into another; somehow we managed to live together in that small space.

CHAPTER 3

AFTER THE CAPTAIN had refused us the chairs, we decided to drag the three canvas-back folding ones and some pillows from our cabin.

Mr. White, the first mate, who had observed us, came along followed by some members of the crew, each gravely bearing a chair like the ones we had.

"Girls, I'm sorry you had to resort to using your cabin chairs, the captain didn't understand that you wanted to sit in the sun; he thought you meant reclining deck chairs like on a big passenger vessel."

He watched as each sailor ceremoniously positioned a chair in just exactly the right place to hopefully catch the bottom of each girl. I'm sure they were wishing they could help ease us into the chairs themselves.

We were profuse in our thanks; now we could spend the fine days reading, talking, and, in Marie's case, knitting. Emma pulled out some needlework too, embroidery and little ribbons that she was using to enhance her sad trousseau. At least we could rest our feet on the rail, tipped back, lined up, pretending we were on a luxury cruise.

I had developed the habit of rising early, slipping into my shorts and shirt, tying a red scarf around my chignon, to sneak on the deck and, holding onto the rail, perform my exercises before the others arose.

I had a need to feel fit, and wanted my husband to find me the same size as the bride he left. I also wanted an occasional change from the unvarying monotony, the mindless banality of conversation, the meditation of staring at the rising and falling sea.

I would be aware of the kitchen crew throwing the garbage overboard, watching the gulls swoop and squabble among themselves for some choice bit.

Try as I would, when alone, I could not stop thinking of my son. My mind was filled with him, his joys and sorrows, his laughter and tears imprinted themselves indelibly in my mind's eye and in my heart. I saw his smile, heard his childish voice, and unbidden tears would come. The girls knew I wrote in my diary every day, and they teased me about it.

"Perhaps I'm writing the great Algerian novel," I would tease back, loath to share with them my feelings about my lost son.

One night at dinner, quite unexpectedly I asked, "Is a husband so important to us women that we would sacrifice our own child for one?"

All heads turned. Here was a subject that had never been broached. Marie's soft brown eyes were tender. "You're missing him a lot, aren't you?"

"You mean you left a child behind to follow a man to another country? You may never see your son again," said Nadia, shocked.

"I had to, his father wouldn't let him go, although he promised right up to the last minute that he would. The very day before we sailed I had to go to court and found out that I couldn't take him. I was so devastated I sat down on the curb and cried and sobbed so loudly that an old man, just a passerby, stopped. I could barely get the words out and this kind person hailed a cab and took me home."

"I could never leave a child behind," said Emma forcefully. Marie concurred, "I told her that already."

Gisèle interjected, "I was abandoned as a tiny baby, perhaps they couldn't help it either, my parents that is."

"If your new husband is as successful as you've let on, perhaps he'll let you go back to see him," ever-practical Lola commiserated.

"I want more than just to see him, I want to be his mother, to raise him as I was meant to. He's only seven years old. Now there's another woman, a new young wife, what does she know about raising children, my child, how would you feel?"

"I never had children, so I can't say," said Arlette, not meeting my eyes. The others nodded. Of course they wouldn't have the frame of reference to know what I was feeling, let alone what I was talking about. Still, I couldn't stop.

"The first bloody nose, the terror that perhaps it's broken, who's going to scratch his head before he goes to sleep, he loved it when his mama did that, you've no idea what it's like, what have I done? It's too late, I can't go back, I can't take it back now. He's starting school, who's going to help him with his school work? We were alone together most of his life, and now he has a stranger for a mother."

On an on I poured out my story, the saga of my lost son, while they sat silently, allowing me my grief.

Gisèle handed me a handkerchief and big-hearted Lola put an arm around my shoulders while

I sobbed aloud, unable to turn off the flood of tears, aware of exposing myself before these women who, although no longer strangers, were not yet friends. They probably were judging me as a bad person, a bad mother.

Arlette glanced over her shoulder, "Please stop, Manola, the men are looking over here and will think something's wrong."

I managed to stifle the few remaining sniffles and said, "The diary I'm writing is for Jean-Pierre; the last thing he asked for was an American train — imagine, he had no idea that I wouldn't be coming back."

"Come on now, you'll show us some pictures of him, won't you?" asked Gisèle.

"Have faith in God," said Marie, piously clutching her little gold cross. "One day you'll meet again, you're a Christian, aren't you?"

"What kind of a question is that," I asked, "of course."

"Well, I wondered, since you wear that Hand of Fatima around your neck, most of us Christians wear a cross."

"My favorite Arab maid gave it to me as a good luck charm," I replied, unaware she had cleverly deflected me from my original subject.

"I noticed none of you pray before you sleep. Why? Don't you offer your soul to God?" continued Marie in the same vein, glancing from one to the other.

"I, for one, have prayed enough to guarantee me a good place in heaven even if I never pray again during the rest of my life," stated Lola emphatically.

"I found through experience that it's what you do on this earth that counts. Prayers may pave the way to heaven, but, if you put all your trust in the Saints, you'll be due for a sad awakening. Believe me, they're not interested in filling your empty belly or giving you a decent bed. If your prayers give you hope, Marie, then by all means please continue and pray for all of us while you're at it."

Lola nudged me with a wink to the others.

Nadia said, "At least we've managed to get this far without being too seasick, except for that first time, we should all be proud of being such good sailors."

"Hah, you don't know what's in store for you," Arlette declared. "We haven't seen a real storm yet, so don't think you're past the worst of it. It's winter, we're crossing the Atlantic after all, so expect bad weather far worse than what we've had so far."

That night was calm and peaceful, my outburst had cleared the way for more open confessions and served me as a cathartic. I felt better, but was still too keyed up to sleep.

As the others, one by one, drifted off, I swathed myself in my blanket, and, crouching on my heels, peered out the open porthole, a pair of eyes guarding the darkness. A lantern swinging from his hand, a tough sailor shambled by in the night. All was quiet except for the throb of the engines and the big, plain, and ordinary cream-colored clock. It was not acting as usual this night. Tick-tocking aimlessly for as long as it could remember, it finally had a purpose: it had never had such charming company and these were its sweetest hours.

I reflected that the smallest things can take on gigantic proportions under the twin influences of the night and the sea. How acutely I noticed the smell of boiling coffee and burning toast, someone must be having a late night snack. I wondered about our journey, were we at least halfway there? I smiled to myself, not knowing the answer.

Things began to take a happier turn when, during dinner, someone produced a record player and records. There were many different styles of music, instrumental, big band, jazz and popular singers. It brightened our mood and stimulated illegal conversation with the officers at the next table who had taken upon themselves the task of educating us to American social mores and customs against the advice of their captain, of course after he had left the mess.

"Who is this Frank Sinatra?" I asked. "I never heard of him." The other girls loudly concurred.

"What do you mean, you never heard of him, he's only the best known singer in the United States," the attractive chief engineer replied with a searching stare at Nadia; the conversation pried open a window of opportunity.

"You'll hear about him a lot in the years to come, I promise you, he's called the bobby soxers' dream."

Nadia engaged the chief engineer in conversation almost every night after that but I never connected anything until I saw her quietly slip out of her bunk and disappear.

"Where were you, for God's sake, I thought you fell overboard," Lola demanded when Nadia finally turned up.

All eyes were riveted on her, awaiting an answer.

Every detail of her flushed face and soft mouth gave the reply without words. Nadia looked as if she had been making love and, judging from her bemused expression and heavily drooping eyelids, most satisfactorily.

She looked from one to another, each female calculating every last detail of her appearance, noting, cataloging, and arriving with lightning speed at the inevitable conclusion.

"And so what?" she barked. "It's not a jail after all, and I felt like it, this voyage is lasting too long without male company, I'm not used to being deprived. But you little pigeons wouldn't know about that, would you? So safe and sheltered, I suppose it wouldn't bother you to be without a man for so long."

As she huskily went on and defended her position, I imagined the scene: the soft knock at the door, quickly opening and closing, when had they managed to make this assignation? No doubt the forced chastity of the men left them vulnerable to the attentions of a beautiful woman, one who had already made up her mind to get what she wanted.

"But you're married," pious Marie protested.

"And what of it?" snapped Nadia. "Besides, my little kitten, it's really none of your business, is it? Just stick to praying and let me be. Don't forget, I am what I am. I've never pretended to be anything different. I like men, I had to use them to live, and when this one isn't around, another one will do. For me, making love is the same as you combing your hair, it means nothing more than the pleasure of the moment. It beats cruising the coffee houses waiting to see who turns up, and, just because I'm married, doesn't mean I can't have a little fling now and then when the opportunity presents itself."

We were silent, shocked. She had alluded to her former life but never this blatantly.

"I recognize how lucky I was to hook some-one who actually wanted to marry me; the other boys from his same company didn't seem so inclined, but when I get together with him, all this will be behind me, I promise you."

"You said your Texan doesn't know what you did before?" I asked more out of fear for her than curiosity.

"No, God forbid, I met Rich shopping, he asked me to help him choose a gift for his mother and I was as demure as you," smiling warmly first at Gisèle and then at Emma.

"Typically male, he never guessed that the red pussy he felt lucky to adopt was a gray alley cat, like we all are at night."

She laughed and somewhat nervously we echoed her — another barrier down, feeling closer to her, forgiving her. Lola seemed to understand Nadia better than the rest of us, perhaps because she had some first-hand knowledge of her poverty-stricken background. We started to pair off, the two loudest and most vulgar, the three little mice together, and Arlette and myself, the two society girls.

When she wasn't embroidering, Emma fid-dled with her pimples, which drove me to distrac-tion.

"Don't squeeze your face like that," I cau-tioned, "you'll just make matters worse. Here, use this astringent," and I handed her my bottle and some cotton.

"You're so kind, Manola, you're not changing again?" Emma as well as the others thought my con-stant clothes parade silly, but it made me feel better not to have to spend all my days dressed the same.

I changed before lunch and before dinner every night.

"I'm a little envious," she confessed, "if I had your wardrobe, I'd probably do it too." That gave me an idea.

"Let's fix you up, come on, I see you in this dress of mine, it's silk and will fit you just right". Its background was black with small flowers in yellow, orange, green and blue, square necklined, long sleeved with a dropped waist. I heaped her generous supply of hair over to one side and tied it with an orange ribbon. It was like dressing a doll, we were alone in our quarters, and I poured my heart into the project, even pulling out my best pair of high heels. Unfortunately, she was such a country girl, she couldn't manage walking in them, her flat-footed stride caused her to stumble and nearly fall. To avoid an accident, I let her wear her own flat shoes, which wouldn't show under the table. I dug through my small cache of jewelry, found long pearl earrings and a little gold choker which complemented the neckline. I powdered over her pimples, added eye pencil and black cake mascara. Her bushy but well-shaped eyebrows I left alone, and, after outlining her mouth and filling in with light Coty lipstick, I stepped back to admire my handiwork. If only her skin had been better, she would have looked like a million. As it was, upon entering the mess hall, everyone stared, wondering who the glamorous stranger was, Lola whistled and even snooty Arlette, said, "Emma, you look lovely tonight," which made her blush, adding yet more pink to her inflamed pimples.

Now that we were allies, I urged her, along with Marie who had to be forced to put down her interminable knitting, to join me doing some simple push-ups off the bulkhead. I was shocked that neither of them had any upper body strength, considering the hard lives both had led. Marie toting heavy trays and Emma with her arduous farm chores had no musculature in their arms at all. My years of daily tennis made me the decided superior, but after a few sessions they were ready to throw in the towel, and so was I, preferring to work alone.

Lola and Nadia must have cooked up something between them because at the close of dinner one evening Nadia urgently whispered to Lola, "Ask him, go on, ask the captain now."

He was seated in sober dignity at the head of his table, stirring his coffee in silence.

Lola sashayed over to him, swinging her hips, a big smile on her painted mouth.

"Captain, couldn't we dance? All that nice music is going to waste. I mean all together? Would you mind?"

He reacted as if he had found a tack on his chair. He looked to his officers for support. Any kind of support, but, lips quivering, they kept their eyes glued to the empty plates in front of them. He turned an intimidating glare on Lola, the same glare that had cowed ships' owners, agents, and refractory crews.

"Well, can we?" she repeated, her smile broadening.

His thoughts were visible on his face. He knew full well what dancing could lead to. He had not shipped out of all the ports of the world not to imagine what could happen when the male and female bodies made contact. But everybody danced. How could he justify a refusal of what appeared to be an innocent request? He knew better. This was no innocent request from his fragile cargo, for such was what he thought. His duty was to deliver this cargo to its destination in good condition. He was responsible for its chastity and felt inadequate to the task of policing its activities twenty-four hours a day.

By this time, Louis Armstrong was blaring from the record player and Lola continued to press the beleaguered captain for an answer, even slipped off her shoes, grasped her full skirt and improvised some steps to illustrate what she meant.

"Please say yes, Captain, come on, what do you have to lose," she pleaded.

Suddenly, as if someone had flicked a light switch, the room filled with electricity and the tension exploded into more noise, the men clapping in time to Lola's dance. Her tempo increased, her whirling skirt revealed even more of her muscular thighs.

The captain scowled at his mutinous officers as Lola squealed in anticipation at the outcome of her plan; without missing a beat she bent over and planted a noisy kiss on his perspiring nose. We girls all applauded and Lola, daring even more, seized the poor captain by one arm, endeavored to hoist him to his feet, her seductive motions beckoning him to dance.

His command was in danger, never in his life had anyone ever taken such familiar license with his position and, feeling as if doused with ice-water, he leapt to his feet and bellowed like a discharging cannon.

"This has gone far enough!"

The officers stopped dead in their tracks, frozen in the act of trying to push back the tables and chairs to make a bigger space for general dancing.

"This is a ship at sea, not a nightclub. Kindly remember who you are, the wives of servicemen, not dance hall hostesses. I told you before that I am the law on this ship and that there will be no fraternization with the crew and I meant it."

He turned to his shamefaced men. "I expect you to obey your orders and remember your positions as officers of this ship. You know my feelings on mingling with the women."

Glowering once more in our direction, he lowered his voice and very distinctly and coldly ordered, "I would suggest you retire to your cabin now that you have finished dinner." He dismissed us like an unruly class of children and re-seated himself.

We were a cowed bunch leaving the mess hall. Even Lola was at a loss for words. We crossed the aft-deck and, after a quick and chilly glance at the moon, sought our cramped refuge where, without words, we got ready for bed, climbed into our bunks and fell asleep — or pretended to.

As if heralding an ominous turn, the wind whipped up the sea, probably in response to our chastisement from the captain. Shuddering, the ship nosed down into the trough of oncoming waves, groaned, and righted herself again. I lay in my top bunk quietly listening, dozing slightly. The wind pounded the waves, which in turn pummeled the ship's sides reverberating in the stillness, and served as a counterpoint to the sounds of my sleeping companions.

I sat up hearing something else, it sounded like sobbing. "What is it?" I whispered, wondering if it could be the haughty Arlette, since it came from her bunk.

"Are you awake too, Manola?"

"You want to talk a little, Arlette?" I asked. "Come and bring your blanket and sit up here with me. We can watch the sea, if you don't want to talk."

She climbed up, settled down, blew her nose, and said, "I was never so embarrassed in my life when the captain addressed us like little children, how demeaning!"

"I thought so too, but of course he was under the impression Lola meant for us girls to dance together, you know, like at boarding school."

She giggled, sounding girlish and natural.

"I'm curious about you, Arlette, you never mix with the others, they all think you're a snob."

"Well I *am* a snob, and so what? But how about you? I know you're an educated girl, did you study abroad?"

"No, but I have traveled outside of Algiers, I have gone to Paris every year with my parents and to India once or twice with my father, what about you?"

"I never finished at the Sorbonne, but I studied science there for two years. I really just wanted to get married and leave Algeria."

"Where do you come from then, originally, I mean."

"I was born and partly raised in Oran where my father is a wine grower. He owns the largest vineyard in the region. I'm an only child and spoiled rotten, as you can see."

She giggled again, and in spite of myself I warmed to her.

"You don't look like a woman from Oran. You dress elegantly and are made up tastefully. The Oranese are flashy, wear too much makeup and jewelry. My cousins are perfect examples. We all used to poke fun at how they looked and how they talked and how loud they were. You're not like that."

"I thank my father for my good education," she said. "Although, when I'm at home, I sound just like them, the voices rising and falling, we always thought it was musical."

The wind was really howling now and we huddled deeper into our blankets. Rain was falling and beating at the porthole for admission. Situated as we were in the stern, directly over the propeller, we noted every change of the ship. Each wave which assaulted the hull made itself felt in the vibration which passed through to our bodies. We both tensed to meet these changes while chatting, swaying like roller coaster riders: first a slow upward climb, then a moment when the ship hesitated as if trying to decide what to do next, followed by a sickening swoop downward. We would brace ourselves for the next labored ascent knowing that it would be followed by yet another inevitable downward swoop.

"I noticed you weren't sick when everyone else was, and you aren't going to be sick now, are you?" I asked.

"No, I'm as good a sailor as you are. That's how I knew we had a lot in common, had traveled on large ocean-going liners before. I don't think you'll get sick either."

"I was a resistance fighter during the war, so not very many things can make me sick," I replied soberly.

"I'm sorry you had to leave your son, he's awfully cute."

My eyes filled involuntarily. She noticed and changed the subject. We chatted on about, "Who do you know," and when I asked her how she had met her colonel she said, "pure chance, I was a hostess at an officers' get-together at the St. Georges Hotel, and someone introduced us. I must say I liked the way his uniform fit and he was heavily decorated which is why I laughed — and it was mean of me — when Marie said her G.I. was a war hero. Mine really does have a lot of medals. He's older than me, quiet, and losing his hair a little, but those things don't really matter when you know he can give you a good life. He must be an important man because I gather his family owns one of the biggest retail stores in New York." As she talked on about her Charles I reflected that medals and a uniform don't make the man and also that Arlette seemed the type of woman who, if disappointed in her choice, would move on without regret.

Little by little we grew sleepy and by the time she climbed down and turned into her bunk I was asleep.

Like the eye in the middle of a hurricane, the day dawned bright, with scudding clouds, alternately obscuring then revealing a watery sun. With feathery wisps of intermittent rain, it appeared that part of the storm had passed over us.

Our days had fallen into the routine of breakfast, lunch and dinner and because of the wet weather I was unable to exercise, yet felt the need of it very badly. Marie knitted, Emma sewed, I read and wrote, tried to keep fit, but the others had nothing but gossip to occupy themselves between meals and we were together all the time for lack of anywhere else to go; occasionally tempers flared like a brush fire, but as quickly burned themselves out.

CHAPTER 4

THE EXPECTED STORM materialized with a fury. I stepped out on deck and gaped in amazement. Across the immensity of sky, tremendous cloud masses formed and re-grouped. They loomed like mountains, then, driven by the wind, split apart only to form other and more enormous peaks and crags. The sea had risen to meet the clouds and, as far as I could see, gigantic waves hovered over them dwarfing the frail ship. Now the rain began in earnest, drenching us as we reeled out en route to lunch.

Lola and Marie were already touched by the motion, and, with the extra element of fear added, they clung to each other, their faces a sickly green, and in unison lurched to the rail. They were soaked, but too weak from retching and unable to ask for help, caught like flies on a spider web, clinging to the only solid object within their reach that would hold them upright.

"Here, let me help you," I screamed into the wind, and, since no one offered to assist me, I pried their grasping fingers from the rail; hanging onto one while I unhooked the other, slipping and sliding, I guided them back to safety.

They were too sick and incoherent to say very much, but I tried to get them out of their wet clothes and into their bunks where they moaned and shivered, Marie praying aloud for deliverance, to which I couldn't help adding my "amen".

I didn't like to leave them alone, but the storm had sharpened my appetite. Taking a deep breath, knowing I was as wet as I could possibly be, I ran to the mess hall.

The other four shared a smug superior look. They had survived while the weak had fallen by the wayside. They were self-congratulating, feeling themselves above the vulnerable lesser mortals. Each displayed her finest manners, resolutely determined that the odors of food wafting from the swinging kitchen hatch would not upset the already tenuous hold on their stomachs. The meal was eaten as a religious rite. No one lingered over the usual second cup of coffee to chat, but, as soon as they had finished, rose and began the trek back to the cabin. What began as a stately parade nearly ended in a rout. When we reached the deck, the ship's movement became more pronounced. Nadia made an inarticulate sound and, without ceremony, scuttled to the rail and heaved up into the closely foaming sea everything she had eaten. She continued to retch long after her stomach was empty, but the others, concentrating on warding off the queasiness that had attacked them, tried to pay no attention, left her there, and staggered across the slippery deck to the cabin.

While they took cover, I looked back to be sure Nadia was not swept overboard. She had let go of the rail, sunk to her knees, her body mindlessly following the ship's gyrations. She rolled over onto her face, and, although I couldn't hear her, I knew she was moaning and calling for help. I waited for the ship to come about, ran back and knelt beside her. Remembering my first-aid course during the war, I slapped her on both cheeks until her indignant mumble told me she was alert. I wrestled her to something of an upright position and, tottering under her dead weight, tried to drag her to the cabin. She was rubber-legged, like a drunk, and we tacked back and forth, gaining, then losing ground, until I was at the point of letting her go and letting myself sink to the deck next to her. I gritted my teeth and, just when I had reached the limit of my endurance, we arrived at the cabin hatch. The cabin reeked of vomit. There was no point in trying to clean up. Every time I thought of helping yet another victim to at least change her clothes, she would be off again, either out the door or to the head, where, if anyone wanted to use the toilet for legitimate purposes, they couldn't have. Arlette and I were the least affected, but even we didn't feel all that terrific. The others, the sickest, turned their faces to the wall, covered their heads and wished for death, some more audibly than others. Marie had stopped praying; probably for the first time in her life she was too sick to call on God to save her, she was also in no position to make the sign of the cross over anyone else either. With the comings and goings from the head, we decided to leave the light on all night.

The heavy waves continued to batter the hull; the ship, like a paper boat on a stream, pitched and rolled, yawed and heeled.

Even with all the sickness and the ship's activity, when the long hours stretched around to dinner time, Arlette and I alone were able to sprint to the mess hall. Our table was not the only one with empty chairs.

"Look, even the captain and the first mate with the gigantic appetite are missing," I remarked.

I wanted a walk desperately, but to be out in such heavy seas was foolish and I wondered where we could go to get away from the evil smell of our cabin which was sure to assail our nostrils afresh after the open air.

I called Billy our waiter over, "Can you ask the cabin boy to come with a mop and bucket? We've had a number of accidents in our cabin."

He smiled knowingly.

Hour by hour the poor old *Bald Eagle* inched westward across the stormy waters against the opposition. For a few minutes at a time there would be a respite, the wind and waves would abate and those of us still coherent could relax a little, but all too soon the mad cycle of slow climb and swift descent started all over again and we tightened our muscles to await the adjustment we had to make. There was little talk, everyone just wanted to be left alone to die.

In spite of the violence of the storm hurling showers of spray against the bulkhead where our portholes were located, I was sorely tempted to open mine, if only for a few seconds to rid the miasmic air of the stench of acrid vomit, exhalations of seven humans, both breath and body odor. I wasn't really that sick yet myself, but, at the rate the others were fouling the atmosphere, I would be soon. Such was the pattern for six or seven full days and nights. I lost count and soon found myself nursemaid, mother's helper, waitress, guardian angel and door guard to the others as they, in turn, got better then worse, better then worse.

Each morning dawned pale and ghostly. I was in charge of the light switch that helped alleviate the gloom of the dismal cabin as well as our mood.

Returning from a hurried breakfast one morning the overpowering odor finally broke me. I seized one of our deck chairs, flung the hatch wide, and propped it open.

Amid screams of "it's cold," and "shut the door," I announced that, since the wind was flinging spray from the north side, there was little chance of us drowning in our bunks and we needed air desperately. I maintained my watch at the door for an hour, by which time fresh air had enlivened the occupants somewhat and cleaned out some of the stench.

During another solitary breakfast I observed agitation among the officers in the mess. Some bolted their food, and hurried out the hatchway, others arrived hastily, bent down to whisper in the captain's ear, then huddled in a small group arguing quietly with glances over to me as if they were hiding something. Were we in danger, I wondered? I felt a heightened sense of excitement, some drama unfolding, but so far I was an audience in the dark, not privy to their secrets. I decided not to tell the other girls, no need for alarm, false or otherwise.

Against the captain's express orders, I enlisted the aid of our waiter, Billy, to help me get some food into the sickest. No one had been to the mess hall for days, and I was really afraid they would suffer malnutrition, starvation or succumb to their illness.

"The ocean during the North Atlantic winter isn't for fair weather sailors," said the captain and decreed that, "unless they can come here to the mess for meals, they don't eat." But Billy and the cook worked out a way that, when the captain was asleep or on the bridge, I could slip into the galley and the cook would give me soup, peppermint tea, bouillon and other liquids that would hopefully stay down in the stomachs of the victims.

It was in this manner that I managed to keep the little band of war brides alive. The clear rich broth somehow stayed hot on my perilous journeys across the slippery deck and noses twitched as I ladled the steaming soup into cups that I took out of my pockets. The strongest pulled themselves upright in their bunks, and even the weakest turned to face the source of the delicious aroma that battled for supremacy over the reeking smell.

"I always heard dry crackers were good for morning sickness," said Nadia gratefully. She munched hungrily, her face pale in the dim light.

The storm raged on. I lay cocooned in my bunk comfortable enough not to attempt getting up until I absolutely had to. The mumblings and movements of my cabin-mates did not intrude as I thought about this strange journey and its stranger destination. For the first time I allowed myself to speculate, looking forward instead of backward. And why not? Even with the storm, we must be making some headway getting there.

A particularly violent lunge of the ship brought a volley of oaths from Lola in a mixture of French and Arabic and trailed off into muttered expletives railing against the fates responsible for her misery. I smiled to myself. Here was one of the dauntless. The vicissitudes of life might bring her to her knees temporarily, but she would rise to fight again.

I stood over her bunk in the gloom, stared, then had to rub my eyes and stare some more. I couldn't believe it. The top of Lola's head was as hairless as a billiard ball, startlingly white against the once-tan skin of her face. The rest of her luxuriant black curls was gray which must have meant there was a wig lacking, hopefully at the bottom of her bunk.

She opened her eyes, looking deeply into mine. Within a heartbeat we reached a complete understanding. We sighed simultaneously as if we had been holding our breath, then giggled together like two schoolgirls. "It was typhoid, you know?" her eyes continued to search mine.

"It's all right, don't worry." Her secret was safe with me.

The heaving and rolling of the deck beneath my feet made a proper toilette difficult, much less have a real shower, but I tried to keep as clean as possible in case I succumbed to the same seasickness as my companions. I didn't want to be found as unkempt as they were.

This was positively the very last day I was able to negotiate the treacherous deck with my small amount of liquid and comfort. The storm's fury rose again, and, to complete our already existing misery, something new had been added. When the poor belabored ship reached the trough, she hesitated a moment or two and then, propeller shuddering, rang like a gong, as tons of water broke and poured over her stern, threatening to engulf the cabin in which we lay. This was getting serious enough for me to seek help.

"Captain, we have to move those sick girls somewhere warm and dry or they're all going to fall seriously ill now that the water is coming inside."

Glaring at me as was customary, his eyes frosty with dislike, he slammed his fist on the mess hall table and growled, "Damn, I can't turn my ship inside out for the sake of a bunch of seasick females. Blast those idiots that had to pick me to convey their passengers, I told them it would mean trouble. We're not equipped, especially with a vessel that should have gone to dry dock months ago. Where am I supposed to move them, for godsakes? There is no place, they'll have to do the best they can, no one ever died of seasickness, please be assured of that."

"But Captain," I protested, "the seas are so violent now, the water is washing inside over our floor and they're cold and wet, and could catch something serious."

"This is a full-size atlantic gale in case you haven't noticed, all my attention has to go where it's needed, which is piloting this tub through the storm, and we haven't seen the worst of it yet, so don't bother me with trifles."

I should have known better than to ask the captain for anything. Ever since our arrival he had taken an extreme dislike to me, perhaps the incident of the iron and ironing board made him feel I was insignificant and didn't deserve his respect. I wondered what to do.

The very next day the first mate came, disheveled and looking tired. His eyes were red-rimmed like the captain's had been when I accosted him to move us.

"It's a terrible storm we're in, girls, and I came to tell you that we may have to move you off the stern."

We all hung on his next words.

"We're sailing west and the ship has been exposed on the right, or starboard side, to the enormous swell that is being whipped up by the wind from the north. We never made it to dry dock and we're aware of problems with the welding; as a result we've developed a large tear which is letting in heavy seas and exposing the ship to the gale on the stern affecting this cabin. Captain has ordered the nose turned south, so the waves which now strike amidships will have this cabin awash with gale force seas and you could all be swept away."

Gisèle moaned, "I don't care, the sooner it happens the better for me."

He continued, "Just be prepared to make a move at a moment's notice, leave everything but your mattresses and blankets, bundle up warmly, wear all the clothes you can."

"When?" we chorused.

"Probably before nightfall. Just be ready."

Against the protests of the sickest I wheedled and argued them into their clothes. I was still the only one standing.

Later, needing air, I wrestled with the hatch which the screaming wind nearly tore from my grasp. The scene which greeted me would have daunted even the bravest. Coils of rope and other debris littered the deck, impeding passage. The passage of anyone crazy enough to venture out, that is. The ship lay at the bottom of a valley, walled on both sides by the most gigantic waves I had ever seen. They loomed over us like mountains. She nosed furiously like a mad dog, and shook. A quick look behind me produced a vision of other mountains, curved at the top, which threatened to totally engulf us.

I wanted to slam the hatch shut but a shout alerted me to three bulky figures in oilskins making their way into the gale, hand over hand down the deck. It was the first mate and two seamen who rolled the girls' mattresses and blankets in black tarpaulins. Slowly, they timed their descent to the deck house by the pitch and roll of the waves, each supporting one girl between them, taking their charges away from danger. Finally they were all gone but me.

Alone, the first mate made the dangerous journey once more.

"You're the strong one. As we have limited room, the captain ordered only the sick to be moved. Do you think you'll be all right here alone? As it is, I don't know where we're going to put them all."

He looked worried. I'm sure he was wondering if I could weather this worst part of the storm by myself.

"As long as I don't get sick, I'll be fine," I assured him. "I'm not afraid, and the storm can't last much longer, can it?"

"I hope not. I'll check on you later if I can get away. We're all pulling double watches because of the danger to the ship, so be good and don't venture out to the mess alone, I'll come for you when I can."

Alone at last, I savored the peace and comparative quiet of the groaning superstructure of the ship. My nursemaid duties and their excitement had carried me through, but now I was at the end of the line. I thought I could try to clean up a little, but the exhaustion from dragging the sustenance across the deck under such conditions for so many days had finally caught up with me. I really didn't feel well and hoped that the kind first mate wouldn't return that night so that I could miss dinner and sleep. The shrieking of the wind lulled me and the size of the unshared cabin seemed suddenly too large; in spite of myself the missing companions made me more aware of the creaking of the laboring vessel.

The first mate didn't come that night, but apologized profusely in the morning. He hadn't been able to get away. I didn't care, the lightheadedness I had noticed the night before had not vanished with sleep. I was in another world and I certainly didn't want breakfast, but allowed him to half carry me through the howling wind and deck debris to the mess.

Someone had rigged a curtain to shield the girls as they lay in a row on their mattresses. Now it was Billy's turn, when he was not busy waiting on the others in the mess room, to coax them to eat what they could and try to drink.

It was warmer and quieter there than our drafty and damp cabin and I almost wanted to move in with them but there was no room for me.

I had developed a bad headache and a ringing in my ears. I only wanted to lie down, even in the moldy cabin which was beginning to take on more and more water.

Alone again the second morning, I awoke on fire with a dry mouth. A fever — my hand strayed to my upper buttocks where I felt twin aching and throbbing swellings.

"Boils," I said out loud. I had firsthand knowledge of this familiar and painful condition. Not enough fresh fruit and vegetables during the entire war, canned food, cured and heavily preserved and chemically treated meats, and now this journey. Oh well, some penicillin and I'll be fine, at least that's what they would have done back home.

Muzzy with fever, glassy-eyed and pale, I stared at my image in the mirror. I dragged myself out to the hatch where I was nearly blown away, I had put on every article of clothing I owned, but was wet clear through from sweat. I lost all sense of time and huddled, teeth clattering, beneath my blanket.

As little as I was aware, dreams and reality merged, but I saw the luggage and chairs floating, which meant the situation was growing critical. In my delirium I worried about my favorite Paris hats that I had insisted upon taking with me. I also worried about my wooden tennis racket in its wooden press down there on the floor, how would water affect the cat gut strings? I would not be able to stay much longer in this self-imposed exile. I lost track of time, days even, but was dragged awake by a thunderous rhythmic thumping.

I weakly called "come in" hoping to be heard above the storm. The first mate in black rubber boots opened the hatch as the imprisoned water rushed out past him. He kicked his way through the flotsam of chairs, suitcases, and other paraphernalia to my upper bunk where he loomed above me, only his eyes twinkling under the wide brim of his sou'wester.

"Is it your turn now?" he joked.

One close look froze his smile, making him serious.

"You're not seasick, you're really sick," he exclaimed as he put an icy hand on my burning forehead. "Wow, what a fever you've got, poor thing, all alone for two days, I haven't been able to come and you've missed meals, which worried all of us. The first thing is to get you out of here."

He swooped me up, blankets and all, and,

hooking the hatchway shut with one big rubber heel, he dashed and slid across the deck as fast as he could for safety.

In the light of day, he could see my pallor and whistled, "You really look terrible, what are we going to do, and where can I possibly put you now?"

I was sitting sidesaddle on the chair he dropped me in; by this time the twin boils were more than a casual irritation. I hurt all over and could feel the toxins spreading throughout my body, I was almost past the point of caring.

"Where are the others?" I mumbled.

"Never mind about them. They're well taken care of. We officers doubled up so that the girls could have our cabins. Now stay right where you are, and I'll try to find someplace for you."

I drifted off, perched well to the front of the hard chair, swaying slightly in my fever. He hurried back, and, once again lifting me as if I had been a child, carried me down a dimly lit passage to a cabin where he lowered me carefully to a bunk on the floor level. He pulled up the blankets around my shoulders, where, turtle-like, I shrank, teeth still chattering. I didn't remember him leaving. My ears were so clogged that the two voices reached me as if I was underwater.

"You should have asked me first," the annoyed voice said.

"I'm sorry, there wasn't time, the woman has a very high fever. I had to do something."

"Well, what's wrong with her? For God's sake, don't you realize you displaced a colonel's wife? I'll have the brass on my back for sure now, explaining that one."

"Don't worry, the colonel's wife doesn't know

what's going on around her. She just needs a place to lie down. Her seasickness is not as crucial as this one's fever and, if she turns out to be infectious, she will have to be isolated anyway."

The irritated voice rose, "I know, but next time ask first, for God's sake. I'm just surprised you didn't put her in my cabin, what's next?"

"When she wakes up, I'll try to find out what's wrong with her, perhaps she's going to need some penicillin to fight this thing."

"Oh no, you know my feelings on that subject. The medicine we carry is in short supply and only for the crew. I'm sure she'll be all right without it. She looks strong enough. I'm not parting with one single ampoule, so forget about it."

I must have faded out again, because the next memory was pain, acute pain where the boils were. Two men were trying to pull me upright and attempt to wedge a pillow down behind my back.

"Here, drink this," Billy said, his brown face beaming at me.

He tried to force a mug of steaming coffee into my hands, but I could only think about the pain in my buttocks.

"The cook and I were just talking about how good you were doing, and now you get sick on us too."

"I'm not seasick," I protested, "I have an infection, and a fever, and I'm sorry, I can't drink this coffee."

"Come on now, missy, you haven't had anything to eat in days, and if you're not going to eat, I'm going to tell the captain and you know what he's like."

Dimly I remembered the conversation above

my head. What was that about penicillin being only for the crew? What had started out as a minor inconvenience was now a raging problem and I was afraid. I pleaded with Billy to get the first mate and once again drifted off to a dreamland peopled with ogres and witches.

"How are you feeling?" asked the first mate solicitously. "You really are scaring me, you look terrible and your fever is making you rave, I heard you. Can't you tell me what's wrong?"

Hesitantly, embarrassed, I plucked at the blanket, not looking at him. I blushed furiously, then in a rush the words all tumbled out.

He smothered a smile. "Boils are never pretty and always very uncomfortable, I don't suppose you would allow me to take a look for myself? You know we have no doctor on board, but I have some experience with these things and I think I could help."

I hesitated again, feeling vaguely uncomfortable, which he must have sensed as he pointed across the room. "In that bunk are two of your companions. Although they're still fairly out of it, you can feel safe, we're not alone in this cabin."

Reassured, I nodded.

"O.K., turn over on your stomach, just pretend I'm an old doctor with a long white beard and let's have a look."

I stared into his blue eyes; they expressed only concern and I complied.

He poked and prodded around the area which hurt and I winced.

When he was finished I rolled over with some difficulty and he helped me to a sitting position, well away from the bulkhead.

"Well?" I asked.

"They're certainly beauts, I'll agree with that. And the placement is weird. The ones I've seen before have either been higher or lower down, but yours don't have to apologize for size to anyone's. They're due to pop, but we can't wait because the infection could spread throughout your body and we can't have that, can we? So this is what I propose. The captain will not allow penicillin to be wasted on the passengers, I'm sorry. I could go behind his back, but, since we've discussed it already, he would know and take reprisals if I went against his orders, so...," and his voice trailed away.

"So?" I asked.

"So our only option is to open them up, clean them out, sterilize the area and get you well as soon as possible."

I nodded.

"It'll be painful, but it's the only method we follow at sea when they get as inflamed as yours are. Even with the storm raging, I think we mustn't wait. Can you stand it?"

"I want to feel better."

"You'll be on your feet within twenty-four hours, I can guarantee that. Now listen, this is how we're going to do it. I will cut open the boils, I will put a lot of heavy pressure on you to express the pus, and then we'll use a very strong antiseptic to wash out the wounds and leave them clean. What do you say?"

He sounded confident and I felt it. He evidently had done this before and I was not really afraid.

"Yes, let's do it, when?"

His face broke into the first smile I had seen in a long time. He leaned over, patted my cheek and said, "I should've known you were a brave girl. All right then, I'm going to try to do it this afternoon in between my watches. I'll bring the second mate to help and we'll relieve you of these boils, but bear in mind, it *will* hurt, you'll have pain but it'll soon be over."

I was familiar with pain, but I didn't want to tell him that the average woman can handle pain far better than the male of the species. Why else were we chosen to bear children? All the beatings I had survived at the hands of my drunken husband, the painful loss of both my parents, the deaths and horror of the war, oh yes, pain and I were old acquaintances.

After he left, I stared at the ceiling and reflected on those miserable periods of my life. I was aware of breathing in the bunk across the way and made out two forms, intertwined in each other's arms and, in spite of conditions, I smiled at the picture of proud Arlette wrapped around little Gisèle the mouse.

The two men arrived with clean towels, a basin and some bottles. They moved quickly and quietly.

"Turn over, Manola, we're going to sterilize the site."

I gave a little gasp at the icy shock and tried to joke. "Have you kept that in the refrigerator just for me?"

Mr. Watson, the second mate, presented me with a hairy forearm.

"Now, if you have to scream when he cuts you, bite down on this, we don't want the old man to find out what we're doing or we'll end up in the brig."

I realized that they were putting themselves in jeopardy for me and I was touched enough that I wouldn't give them away for anything.

I had to flinch at the sharp attack of the razor cutting into the boils but the hand wielding it was sure and swift and the momentary agony was followed by relief at the eruption of the boil and the discharge. It hurt more when his strong fingers expressed the contents which exploded with a pop into the ready towel. Then the sting of what smelled suspiciously like whiskey poured lavishly into the wound.

"That's one," he announced.

"Is that whiskey I smell?" I asked, spitting the second mate's arm hair out of my mouth.

"All we could find as an antiseptic, it's good stuff, so don't worry."

He swiftly made short work of the second boil in the same manner as the first, taking care to wipe away the excess whiskey when he was through.

To finish the procedure, he applied an improvised bandage made of overlapping layers of gauze.

The bed smelled of whiskey and I joked, "Tonight, when I sleep, I'll dream of whiskey and water, the way we drink it in India."

"There, that wasn't so bad, was it?" my blue-eyed savior asked smilingly.

"Not even a scream," commented the second mate admiringly.

"Thank you both," I replied gratefully. I had relief and knew I would start to feel better soon.

"You'll want to leave the dressing on, and not get it wet. Here are some extra bandages, perhaps one of your teammates can help you put them on, and, when you arrive in California, have a doctor check you out just in case." They left as quietly as they had arrived and I slept heavily to awaken with no fever, no throbbing head. The glands in my throat were no longer swollen and the general malaise was gone.

"Good morning," I said out loud, hoping to awaken Gisèle and Arlette in the next bed. They stirred but didn't answer.

This cabin was wood paneled in a light color and was nicely appointed with a desk and several shelves of books. My host had also a large bathroom with shower, sink and other amenities, that much I could see through the open door. Now that the fever wasn't distorting my senses, I could make out details, even the lemony furniture polish was pleasant in its homeyness. The wind and sea seemed far away and I reveled in the peace and quiet and comfort of the wider and stable bunk.

Billy the waiter stuck his head around the open hatch. He bore a tray with good things on it and I sniffed appreciatively.

"Now I want you to eat it all, you hear me?" he demanded. I didn't need to be told twice, I had never been so hungry in my life.

Gisèle and Arlette were recuperating. Arlette seemed a little put out to discover me not only in "their" cabin but also in "her" berth.

I explained what I had gone through, but she pulled away and we all started to dress.

Finally the bulk of the long storm passed over us, the cabin boy armed with mop and bucket cleaned our cabin and, as soon as we were able, immediately in my case, we moved back to our own quarters. The others were getting better too, as evidenced by the rising complaints about the food.

Now that we had tasted the comparative luxury of the officers' accommodations, we were loath to return to our squalid and cramped habitat.

CHAPTER 5

ALTHOUGH THE SWELLS were still running high, breaking and foaming over our deck, the wind was no longer an unseen, implacable force howling viciously through the superstructure of the ship. As the weather improved, so did we. Most of us were strong enough to leave our beds. No one but poor Billy the waiter had time nor patience to listen to our complaints and bore the brunt of our displeasure. The trip was taking too long and we were on each other's and our own nerves.

Finally a day dawned when the sky was clear except for a few scudding clouds and the *Bald Eagle* rode the waves instead of having them thunder down on her decks. It was cold, a brisk, bracing sort of cold, and we all felt better for it. I tried to resume my morning exercise routine and hardly felt any discomfort from my bad experience. I hoped to interest my cabin mates in some physical activity after their long illnesses, but, once again, no takers. Only Marie with her never ending knitting had something to do. Nadia jeered at Emma's efforts to embellish her poor lingerie to make it look nicer. "It's feminine," she explained, but Nadia said out loud that it was a waste of time, and that was because she could think of lots of other ways to spend her days. I wrote to my son, kept up my diary and made better friends with the first mate.

The ship had slowed until she was barely

71

moving through the water. Metal clanged against metal. Orders were shouted and the crew hurried to and fro. A scaffolding had been rigged on which first the captain and his mates, and then the chief engineer and his assistants had been lowered.

From then on, every night after dinner, the main table in the mess was cleared and plans spread out to be discussed. We were all perishing with curiosity. What was going on?

"As you know the storm caused some damage to the hull. The big crack that separated the plates needs to be repaired. We'll shut down the ship's engines with the exception of the navigational equipment so we'll be dead in the water. There's nothing to be alarmed about, girls, however we'll be late at least two weeks in arriving at our destination, I'm sorry," the captain said uncharacteristically.

A giant groan went up from everybody, but, true to form, he turned on his heel and walked away amid protests from his little band of passengers.

"I remember that night," I commented. "The rest of you were out cold, but I knew something had happened, they were all so panicky, I guess we're lucky the ship didn't go down."

We hung over the rail to watch the work, but there was little to see and, one by one, we became bored. During the day the captain stayed on his bridge and the chief engineer supervised the repairs. At night the first mate took the watch and one of the assistant engineers directed the men so they could proceed twenty-four hours around the clock, the quicker to finish. We grew used to the constant clanging just like we had grown used to the howling of the storm, now fading into memory.

Occasionally I would run into the first mate

and he would wink conspiratorially; he taught me my first American slang gesture: when he made a ring of his thumb and first finger that signified "O.K.", so when he put a hand on his buttocks and looked questioningly at me, I copied his action and signaled "O.K." the same way he did.

Since my boils had opened a door between us, on the rare times when our mess visits coincided, I felt warmed to this chivalrous man and watched for him, sometimes not even aware I was doing it. In between my diary, writing letters and taking solitary turns around the deck, I was feeling lonely and blue, something the ocean always brought out in me, some unspeakable longing for something, I knew not what.

"Looks like you never saw a moon before." Suddenly, as if in answer to my prayers, there he was observing me.

I laughed. "You shouldn't startle passengers like that, they might fall overboard."

We leaned side by side on the rail watching the play of moonlight on the water.

"I'm taking a break, I think I'm entitled, working like a dog, don't you?"

We spoke about inconsequential things having to do with the ship, the work, the dreaded captain and his other shipmates and, as he bid me goodnight, I realized I liked talking to the first mate — for such was the way I always thought of him.

Whether it was by design or accident he seemed to find me at the rail on subsequent evenings, and little by little my reserve broke down. Under the cover of the moon I found myself telling him little things I would not have dared in the light of day.

I confessed to an inability to sleep and admitted spending a large part of each chilly night wrapped in my blanket in a deck chair.

"Well, that's really silly, you could catch a good cold that way, I have another solution, if you're interested."

"What's that?" I inquired, thinking he was going to offer a sleeping pill or something.

"Look behind you, there's a ladder that leads to the bridge where I'll be on duty in a few moments. I propose that, the next time you can't sleep, you look carefully about you to see no one's watching, then quietly slip up the ladder to the bridge. Just come up quietly, all right, the old man must never hear of it or there'll be hell to pay. The only reason I can invite you is because I'm alone on watch as we're stretched so thin with all officers needed to oversee the repairs. Ordinarily there'd be several of us on watch at night, it's too dangerous with just one man, so in a way, you'd be helping me out by keeping me alert."

I realized he was on night duty and was asking me to break the captain's rules and "mingle" with him.

I hesitated, glanced at his somber face, without a trace of guile nor ulterior motives and took a chance. "All right," I said, "I'll see you the next time I can't sleep."

This became my pattern; as soon as I recognized that another night of tossing and turning in my narrow uncomfortable bunk was unavoidable, I'd lie motionless and wait for the even breathing of my six companions indicating they were deep in the arms of Morpheus.

I had accustomed them to not seeing me

undress. I was sure there was talk about something going on, as several times on approaching this little gathering or that knot of three girls they suddenly stopped talking, and I suspected I was the subject. I didn't care what anyone said, it was innocent enough.

Slipping up the ladder, I'd carefully look about me but I was always alone. Our conversations, stiff at first, gradually took on a life of their own.

"I can hardly wait to see my baby daughter," he greeted me one night; she'd been born while he was on this voyage and he was on fire to get home. "I love my wife and I hope this little one is a carbon copy of her," his face softened at the thought and I almost had a pang of envy for the lucky girl. We talked about my son, how much I missed him, and my misgivings about Bill, his drinking and hemp smoking, his violent temper, his fear of germs. I told him I hardly knew the man I married. He patted my hand in consolation, and left it there, his large palm covering mine.

"What if the captain walks in right now?" I asked.

"No fear of that, he's pounding his ear and has no reason to be on the bridge. I'm not signing on under him again and, since I stand in better with the home office, I should have no trouble getting another ship. He's likely due to be retired out anyway, the bullheaded old fool, so no love lost. There's nothing he can do to me, but he could make the remainder of the trip unpleasant for you, although I can't imagine how much worse he could be."

Pictures always stay in one's memory. Always framed in the wheelhouse window, erect at the wheel, he peered out into the dark of night. The lights hooded over the instruments cast mysterious shadows as I took my accustomed place in the coziness, on a settee bolted to the rear bulkhead. I wondered what turn our almost ritualistic talks would take this night. He scanned his instruments, reached out now and then to adjust the steering wheel keeping the ship facing into the wind. I quietly tucked my legs up under me, admired his blond profile and wished for a pot of coffee. The nights took on a dreamy, almost surreal quality.

Sometimes he pointed out the constellations and told me the names of the stars. Mostly we talked about ourselves, our lives, my fears, his hopes. At other times we fell into a companionable silence and the only sound then would be the slap of water against the ship's side.

One night, he let me steer the great old tub, and as I grasped the wheel doing what he showed me, I shuddered in anticipation, expecting the audacity of my act to have disastrous results. I liked the feeling of his hand over mine, but I recognized the romantic effect of the sea, as well as the danger of awakening the sleeping demon.

"Go to bed now, you're nodding off and we wouldn't want the next watch to find us here asleep, would we?"

That was enough to hoist me to my feet and softly I went back to the cabin the way I came.

I treasured these nights, and regretted even the idea of the voyage ending. I came to dread the arrival as it would mean the end of my relationship with Al, for this was what I now called him when we were alone on the bridge.

I was careful to crawl into bed as quietly as possible, but, of course, the fuel that was fanning the flames of gossip was generously rendered by first one then another of my shipmates who might turn over, wake and see me undressing and getting into bed.

"Are you sleeping with him?" demanded Lola one day after the mate left the mess without a glance in our direction.

"What?"

"I asked you, is he your lover?"

"I might have known you'd think that," I replied. "Only you could have such an idea, of course not."

It's difficult at best to try to slide anything past six pairs of bright inquisitive eyes, particularly when they watch your every word and gesture, and I was aware that they thought something was going on between the first mate and myself.

"I'm ashamed of you to think that of me, Lola. Mr. White and I are just friends."

She hooted loudly, joined by Nadia who said, "All of us are bored from this damned long trip, and we know that he's on night bridge duty but isn't it dangerous, who's watching the wheel?"

Sanctimoniously Marie whispered as she crossed herself, "Aren't you afraid of God watching you? A married woman, after all, doesn't do those things. My husband and I haven't even been together yet, we got married and he left the same day," and she blushed a deep crimson.

Gisèle nodded in agreement, murmured, "me too" but didn't offer any opinion of her own as to my situation. Nor did Emma who sat in disapproving silence, completely forgetting that we had suffered a storm together and come through it unscathed. She glanced around and finally said, "Manola, speak up, if you were just using him to relieve your boredom, I think it's disgraceful, but, come on, we're waiting to hear your side."

My amusement was turning to anger.

"I'm not doing anything, I don't know how you could think that of me. I sleep on the deck in a chair almost every night and, when I can't, I spend some time talking with the first mate and so what? Please keep it quiet because I don't want to get him into trouble with the captain."

"I would never have thought it of you, Manola, you're supposed to be a lady," sniffed Arlette. "Perhaps some of us — with a glance at Nadia — behave like that, but I would never have expected it of someone of your social standing."

That stung, but offended Nadia as well.

"Hey," she glared belligerently down the table at Arlette, her green eyes flashing, "my heart belongs to my Texas farm boy but I've made do with the sexy chief engineer and would do so again, if I had half a chance, don't doubt it," and she laughed. "Ha, I'm not made of stone, and you have your nerve saying that about Manola after all she's done for you, just remember the storm and how she took care of all of us."

Heads nodded in agreement and I could see that perhaps they believed me after all, or at least had the good grace to feel guilty.

Arlette apologized first to Nadia then to me, and, hurt feelings soothed, we let the subject die a natural death. There was no way they were going to completely believe me and I could care less.

During the clandestine meetings that Al and I continued to have, I told him of the girls' suspicions and he laughed out loud.

"I'm not that kind of guy, believe it or not, I really love my wife and I'm sorry the other girls seem to think that all a man and a woman can do together is to jump into bed. Forget it, they can't hurt you."

I realized he was a true gentleman and was more than ever grateful for his friendship.

"Suppose I can't find my husband when I arrive in California?" I asked one night.

"Why would you think such a thing?"

"I don't know, my instincts told me from the beginning not to marry him. He has a violent streak and I can imagine he won't be pleased when I show up empty-handed, I was robbed of everything I had just before I left, and, to top it off, don't forget — he smokes hemp."

"So what, lots of people do, what else bothers you?"

"He had a tattoo," I confessed.

Al laughed. "Again, so what? Lots of sailors wear tattoos, why not a civilian, and a man's man as you've described him."

"Where I come from, only jailbirds wear tattoos and I objected so much he burned it off with acid."

"Wow, he must really love you, Manola; I think your fears are silly."

He reached for my hand and the strong warm pressure reassured me. The thought crossed my mind that, if Bill was more like Al, I would love him unequivocally.

"Al, you know I suffered a lot at the hands of my first husband, the one who kept my son, and I'm afraid I may have made the same mistake with Bill. He's so mercurial, and yet he can be loving and tender, but underneath there's no middle ground, there's this bottomless well of churning anger and trouble and I'm afraid, that's all. I took a gamble coming to America, had I known they would take my son away from me, I would never, never have married Bill. He won't even be there at the dock to meet me when we arrive."

"Why can't he meet you?"

"I don't know, his last letter that reached me at home just before we sailed said nothing, only that I would be met, taken care of, and not to worry. Well, I am worried, what could have happened, do you suppose? It must be very bad or he'd be there, he says he loves me very much, but what kind of a husband is it that can't meet his new wife who has given up so much for him and has come from so far." As usual, tears were streaming down my face, whenever I spoke of my little Jean-Pierre, and I stifled a sob.

"I don't give my love lightly, Al, and, when I love, I love deeply and completely. I hope he will be the same way, but I don't know."

I could tell he wanted to hug me, but didn't. I felt ambivalent, was it the attraction of the man, or the magic pull of the sea? I knew he felt it too, but was careful not to give either of us an opening.

"How do you say 'What time is it' in French?"

He asked me, partly to change the subject, and also to give me something concrete to contribute to our relationship. For many nights thereafter I taught him rudimentary French, including some love phrases for his wife, little terms of endearment that he could call her when they were together again. I was sure he would remember me when he called her "*Ma chère petite femme*" or said

"*Je t'aime*." He had already taught me so many Americanisms I wanted him to have some French in exchange. Had I known the trouble it would provoke later on, I would've been more careful of what I taught.

Although he hailed from New Orleans, he never bothered to learn any French, but as he told such wonderful stories about his birthplace I wished I was going there, at least I wouldn't have had any trouble with the language — or so I thought.

Each day brought new discoveries in the relationship with my cabin-mates. One day I caught Marie passionately kissing a piece of paper.

"What are you doing?" I asked.

Startled, not expecting to be observed, she shamefacedly held out a photograph of a young soldier, full length, posed in front of a cafe. He was squinting and it was hard to see him.

"It's my monkey," she whispered, embarrassed, trying frantically to rub her pale lipstick off his printed face.

"Let me see too," interrupted Lola, snatching the photo from her hands.

"He's cute, Marie, you're a lucky girl to get such a cute one." Generous as always, Lola stepped into the breach.

"Show us yours, Manola," they chorused. I dug into my suitcase and pulled out a snap of Bill, in swim trunks, sitting on the side of a swimming pool.

His muscular arms and chest were very prominent and attracted the girls' attention.

"No chest hair, you know what that means!" exclaimed Nadia. "Not so," I replied, "he's as sexy as they come, believe me." By now they were all crowding around, pushing and shoving, eager to see and have each of us see their husbands. Arlette as usual stayed away from the mob scene, commenting coolly that Bill looked "very nice". She had really not yet forgiven me for my supposed transgression with the first mate.

Lola offered a full length much handled snapshot of a muscular blond hulk in uniform. Obviously she had slept upon the photo which was rumpled and torn.

"My Stefan, isn't he gorgeous?" she purred and we all laughed.

Nadia's Rich, and Emma's Jimmy were both strapping handsome young G.I.s, Nadia's more impressive due to his official M.P. uniform, but Gisèle claimed she didn't have any photos of her husband; somehow I didn't believe her, I felt she was holding something back.

The sharing of photographs brought another surprise. Emma produced a map of the United States that her Jimmy had given her, with her destination, some small town near the capital, Butte, Montana, circled in red.

We spread it out and for many days pored over it for hours on end. Each in turn tried to locate the state, and the city or town where they would be living. They were so far apart we had trouble believing our eyes. Besides, we had no idea where we were currently located, somewhere at sea. Off the Florida coast?
"We could ask," someone said looking at me. Of course I asked Al that night when I joined him on the bridge, but I don't remember what he said.

Emma's little Montana town was a barely visible speck, while Arlette's New York City took up a great deal of room even on such an attenuated map.

We couldn't find Beverly Hills, but Los Angeles was there for all to see, and Texas was gigantic, enormous, even bigger than the entire country we came from.

Arlette was able to figure out the scale and, converting kilometers to miles as we called out numbers to each other, we were appalled and incredulous at the distances between our various destinations.

On the back of the map, cities' populations were listed alphabetically and in wonder we compared one to another. Many of America's cities contained more people than all of Algeria put together.

"How do you get around in a city with eight million people?" marveled Lola.

Marie laughed, "I don't have to worry about that, New Mexico doesn't look as if it's that populated and the biggest city has only 35,000 people compared to Dallas, where Nadia is going."

"No wonder my husband does so well in his store, he has an unlimited number of customers to pick from," whispered Arlette to me. "He said his store, Macy's, was as big as the *Galleries de France* but, judging from the size of New York, it has to be much, much larger." She smiled, satisfied with her choice. I had the feeling that once her colonel's bars came off and he was a civilian like anyone else, she would no longer be so smug.

We took to carrying the map with us to meals, the better to confer with Billy and the cook. Both had something to say about our future homes. We were overheard by the feared captain who unbent and tried to appear more human as the voyage neared its conclusion.

"Judging from your addresses, I can say that

the lucky one who pulled the best fortune is you," indicating me with a jutting chin, "because Beverly Hills is probably the number one richest community in the entire United States."

"More so than New York?" demanded Arlette.

"Oh yes, many New Yorkers live there too, but the wealth per capita is greater for its size than anywhere else in the country, no doubt due to the movies."

Everyone turned to me, smiled, and offered congratulations. It must be true if the captain said so, but I still had a nagging fear, Bill wouldn't be at the dock to meet me, so I reserved judgment until I could see for myself.

The girls were whipping themselves into a fever of excitement at the thought of seeing their men again.

Imperceptibly the weather had been getting more temperate, and we dressed in our summer dresses and appreciated the warmth of the sun on our faces and the soft balmy breezes which almost reminded us of home.

The *Bald Eagle* had sailed south to lessen the effect of the damage on the ship's broken plates, but soon would have to turn her nose north once again.

"This is the Gulf Stream current flowing north from the equator, don't think it'll last," the captain said. "We have to sail north to reach Baltimore, so enjoy the fine weather while you can, it won't be forever. We're nearing our arrival point, so dig out your coats, you're going to need them." We all groaned at the prospect of more bad weather and numbing, aching, biting cold.

My companions were feeling the pinch of arrival, we shared equal amounts of dread, but theirs was mixed with an optimism mine lacked. Their silences stretched longer and longer, their faces tight, their gestures choppy and mechanical. From time to time one turned an affectionate glance upon her neighbor and smiled in commiseration.

I looked at them admiringly. These were pioneers, strong and brave women who, through the ravages of war, had bonded to a foreign mate and now had forsaken their birthplaces for a far away home. Despite the tranquil influence of the sea, we felt an impalpable sense of helplessness. This gave me an idea. Diving into the cabin, I searched through my bag until I found one of the two bottles of Cognac I had brought as a gift for Bill. He would never know I sacrificed one.

I rushed to the galley where I asked the cook to uncork it. Pouring half into another container for the kitchen crew, I made him swear not to tell the captain. I sprinted back to the cabin for some pencils and a pad of paper.

I rejoined the girls on the deck, and announced: "Girls, come on, I just had a terrific plan. We're going to have a drink of Cognac in celebration of our near arrival. We will then write a message, a dream, a wish for our future, whatever we want, on a slip of paper, re-cork the bottle and throw it overboard. Perhaps someone will find it someday."

I took a tentative swig, coughed, as it was very strong, but felt the welcome warmth flow through me. I wiped the neck, and passed it to the next girl who did as I, swigged, coughed, and passed it on. Marie gagged. We had just enough for one good tour of swigs and the precious bottle was empty. For good measure I turned it upside down, shook it violently, then propped it on its neck to dry inside so that nothing could dampen our missives once they were inserted.

Marie said, "Me first, give me the paper." She tore off a corner, small enough to fold in half, frowned, began to write, crossed out what she had written and started again. "Should I tell what I wrote?" she asked.

"No, of course not, it's your secret, your aspiration, your dream." Marie ceremoniously passed the paper to me. I tore off another corner and began to write my very short message. I turned my paper over to put my new address, to my knowledge, I was the only one who did so. In turn each took the paper, tore off their piece and, concentrating like little children in a school test, looked up for inspiration, caught the thought and began to write.

Arlette was finished first and re-read her message before poking it into the bottle. Emma was next and upon inserting her message, with a constricted throat, whispered, *Inshallah*, as God wills.

Tongue protruding, concentrating for all she was worth, Gisèle wrote her few lines, folded the paper into thirds and inserted her message. Marie continued to scribble, Arlette muttered, "Are you writing your life's story there, or what?"

"Here we go," said Nadia and pushed hers in too. Lola had a hard time with her composition; finally she smiled contentedly, reached for the bottle and we all waited for slow-poke Marie to finish.

"Now we have to seal it so it won't leak," I said, taking the bottle and racing off to the galley where my gift was being appreciated by the entire kitchen crew. Billy and the cook sealed it for me with a strong cork, candle-wax and wire, and I proudly bore it overhead to my little band of companions.

"Who should throw it?" I asked.

"It's your bottle, you throw it, Manola, and we'll each think our message to ourselves as you do."

We stood at the rail; I heaved the bottle overhand as hard and far as I could throw. Straining for the last view, eyes filled with tears from the stinging wind, we watched as the brave little craft, filled with such hopes and dreams rocked about, finally stabilized and floated on the waves. We followed it until it was out of sight.

CHAPTER 6

WE WERE WILD with excitement when other ships began to appear in what we had thought was an empty ocean. We seemed to be seldom out of sight of other large vessels and would run to the rail, if not already hanging there, to wave at the little figures that could be seen on their decks. Almost all waved back, giving us a heady warm feeling of welcome.

Al White had shown me Chesapeake Bay on his charts during our final evening together on the bridge. It was an enormous body of water the end of which could not even be seen. Not like what I was used to at home.

We clung to the rail on our last day and jumped every time the *Bald Eagle* blew a blast on its horn, we were so nervous and jittery we would laugh at each other's loss of composure.

Houses and tall buildings lay just ahead and, hearts beating faster, we knew that our voyage was nearly over and our new lives were about to begin. I was sorry to pull in, I had become used to the company of the girls and the first mate and was in limbo between life on shipboard and dry land. Now that the time had come, I was almost filled with reluctance to leave the security of familiar voices, faces, and routine.

The first mate waylaid me as we girls all rushed about getting ready.

"Listen, Manola, I've been thinking. I'd like you to take my sister's phone number in Los Angeles in case you get into difficulty and can't find Bill."

"Thank you very much, it's very kind of you, I hope I won't need to call her. Why do you think I might have any difficulty?"

"A feeling I have, that's all. Your husband's Beverly Hills address sounds too good to be true for a Hollywood gymnasium owner. Take it for my sake, and here's my address too, please drop me a line and let me know how you make out."

He pushed a slip of paper in my hand and, squeezing my arm hard, turned and walked away. Tears came to my eyes at his kindness, how could I forget him?

The ship docked without incident and we all heaved a collective sigh of relief. It was over.

At our last dinner, we had taken care to exchange our new addresses, with many admonitions to write. After the ceremony of the bottle, I hoped we would stay in touch as our shared experiences would not allow us to part completely from each other.

"Girls, we're bonded, we've shared a voyage, a storm, sickness, and weathered them all, please don't let's lose sight of each other." Tears and kisses, hugs and more tears soothed my fears; although my knowledge of human nature was that friendship is relative, like everything else, it rarely lasts.

I envied seeing the other girls trying to pick out their husbands from the throng of people crowding the pier, and I was surprised to see so many waiting for us to land. It was fiercely cold and snow was blowing. Snow, I had never seen it, except in our mountains when we went to ski. I was grateful for the cozy warmth of my once white, now gray, coat and huddled deeper into its collar. The captain had told us about a bad storm which tied up transportation all along the eastern seaboard. Planes couldn't land nor take off.

Arlette turned, hugged me spontaneously and said, "My husband can't come either, I'll bet. New York is a short train ride away, but I don't think he'll be waiting so here's my hotel's address, come and see me for breakfast tomorrow because I'll be all alone, and so will you."

With handshakes all around she swept down the gangplank and out of sight.

Now that our little band was reduced by one, it was Nadia's turn. Spotting her M.P. somehow in the mob, she shrieked, "Rich, Richie, I'm here," turned, rapidly made the circle of goodbye kisses and was caught up in the swirling throng at the bottom of the gangplank. Her handsome soldier caught her around the waist, looked deep into her eyes, and they kissed for what seemed a world's record. After they came up for air, she turned a dazzling smile on us and gave a mock salute with a sideways toss of her red curls and a thumb indicating her "catch" and her pride in him. The way he kept on touching, squeezing and kissing her, assured us it was mutual. I lost sight of them in the crowd. In my heart I wished her well and tried to push away the twinge of envy I felt at her warm reception.

Emma's husband, the rangy cowboy from Montana looked just like his picture, dressed in denim, he swung his plain bride up into the air and kissed her all over her face, she just clung to his neck like a limpet on a rock.

He held her away at arm's length, the better

to see her, his smile wide, his white teeth flashing. I had a sudden vision of Emma, exchanging one farmland for another, this much different from the last, one form of farmwork for another, one country for another. What I wasn't to know until much later was that Emma's new husband had formed some pretty raunchy ideas about what his "Frenchie" should look like, dressed her up in sexy lingerie, and promptly impregnated her before and after showing her off to his family and friends. He thought her beautiful, exotic and as this pattern was to repeat itself many times, to the tune of four boys, I myself was elected to send her sheer black seamed stockings and a black lacy garter belt from Hollywood to replace the black cotton ones her Jimmy had found somewhere in town. I often amused myself by imagining the homely clothesline with baby diapers, intermingled with black sheer hosiery frolicking in the wind like small flags signaling victory. This was a big departure for the girl who tried to shower in her grandmother's long old-fashioned lace-trimmed underdrawers.

Lola stared at every man, almost as if she had forgotten what her Stefan looked like. Occasionally she glanced overhead and my gaze followed hers to the gray lowering sky, as if she expected him to drop out of a cloud. What I could see of her familiar laughing face looked tight and closed, grim with ill-concealed panic.

Marie made the sign of the cross over me, and, as soon as she located her "monkey" in the sea of people below, released her clenched fist from the rail and a long-held breath in a loud exhalation.

"There he is, there's my Johnny," she screamed and lingered a moment longer just for the pleasure of watching him weave his way gracefully, like a dancer, through the crowd to the foot of the gangplank where she sped to meet him. He was nattily dressed in a navy blazer with bright shiny buttons, camel hair overcoat, white silk scarf, bareheaded, his dark blond hair blowing in the wind. He was wispy, slender, handsome and tall, with a generous laughing mouth. He held out both hands, bent over, and chastely kissed her on one cheek. She snatched back her hands and, flinging both arms about his neck, leaped upward throwing her short legs around his waist, forcing him to cradle her round bottom in his hands or let her fall.

He gently set her down, disengaged himself from her torrid embrace, produced a spotless white handkerchief and mopped at her streaming eyes. She loudly blew her nose, he patted her cheek the way one does a child to reassure her, picked up her suitcase and they turned away to leave. He seemed cool, aloof, indifferent, but perhaps he was merely shy, and I remembered that they had yet to have a real wedding night.

My Arab nurses always said I had the gift of second sight. As with many of these heralded gifts, they were never subject to supply on demand. When I wanted to see someone's future, or read another's aura, I couldn't do it, it was only effective when the feeling was spontaneous, the vision unbidden. Now it happened that I had the distinct impression watching Marie trying to make her husband kiss her, that he didn't want to, and not out of embarrassment or a sense of refinement, but rather disinterest. My heart jumped when I realized, whether poor pious Marie knew it or not, she had married a man with bisexual leanings, desires that perhaps even he himself was not completely aware of. Marie's purpose in his life was to be that of a cover-up, he probably didn't have as much love for her, if any, in comparison to her love for him. Try as I might, I couldn't see the end of this and felt only foreboding for her. Marie looked up to him, clung to one of his arms with both of her hands, a marvel to me, as at home, we would never do that for fear of being thought of as a "loose woman" since they were the only ones who had the luxury of showing their emotions in public. How nice it would be to hang on Bill's arm as much as I liked in this new country. I shrugged; Marie's life was going to unroll however the fates decreed; I was glad I didn't have this revelation during our time together, I would have had a hard time disguising my sad knowledge.

Next, my eye was caught by a large group of colored people quietly waiting off by themselves in a little knot. They were obviously dressed to impress, in their best Sunday clothes and I wondered if they might be relatives of Billy, our waiter.

When Gisèle reached the quay, an older heavy-set man detached himself from the group and swept forward to pull her into his arms; she was still holding her suitcase while he kissed her long and passionately. The group surged forward, laughing and joking, hugging each other and then Gisèle. Tears came to my eyes at the warm welcome. I was so happy for her, she had a family of her own at last, and it looked as if they truly would love her.

Why had she not told us her husband was a colored man? Was this why she had not shown his picture? Was she afraid we would have censored her? It didn't matter to me, but perhaps she had not wanted to bear Lola's and Nadia's teasing or Arlette's disapproval. I wished her well in my heart as the noisy group spirited her away, her big husband half-carrying her on his hip, her feet barely scraping the ground. Now, except for Lola still pacing the pier, I was alone on deck. The captain never appeared to say good-bye, but somehow I hadn't expected him to. I searched for the first mate, then realized his way of parting had been to give me his sister's phone number. Bill had arranged for someone to meet the ship; I was afraid to disembark, so stayed at the rail for fear of missing my only link to him.

I gave myself a mental shake to change my mood and observed two women walking briskly up the gangplank, no-nonsense, sensible-shoes type of women. They both appeared to be in uniform, dark colored jackets and skirts, I noted an emblem of some kind on the chest pocket.

"Mrs. Thompson?"

I nodded.

"I'm Mrs. Rice from Travelers' Aid and this is Elaine. Sorry to keep you waiting, but we didn't know until just this morning when the ship would get in, and your husband was anxious we be on hand to meet you. All the transportation is tied up due to the storm and the heavy quantity of service-men flying home. I'm sorry you don't have priority, but we've arranged to get you on the first available flight to the West Coast as soon as the storm lifts. You may have to fly out of Washington."

I felt steamrollered by these women.

"We have a hotel room for you, and can change your foreign currency." She reached for my handbag and opened it. I gasped with shock, but she continued to talk while she counted the contents of my wallet which held very little.

"Please don't spend any money foolishly. We'll put some of this away with the hotel desk, whatever is left over at the end of your stay they'll return to you. Your husband indicated that you would be bringing more than this? Now, for meals, there's a neighboring restaurant in the Greyhound bus terminal where you can eat, half a block away at the corner. Let's go get you fingerprinted and your passport taken care of, we'll clear customs and we'll take you to your hotel, I'm sure you must be tired."

What could I reply to such a bossy woman? I was upset at being treated like a little child and I didn't appreciate her way of taking over my money, as little as it was, and her self-importance was most irritating, but I felt an underlying warmth beneath the brusque exterior and allowed myself to be whisked down the gangplank. Lola stopped her pacing long enough to look up and see us.

The Travelers' Aid lady asked her if she needed anything.

"No, no, thank you, I'm just waiting for my husband, he seems to be late, I'm sure he'll be here soon."

I kissed her goodbye. I wasn't sure if the knot forming in my stomach was for myself or for her.

"Shit," she stamped her foot and swore, "where is he?"

At customs, the officer seemed amused by my confusion in understanding his questions. I was so nervous, what little English I had command of deserted me completely. He never bothered to open my bag, I could have been smuggling hashish for all he knew. At immigration I produced my documents, which found favor with the kindly officer. He rose, leaned over the desk and actually welcomed me to the United States with a handshake. I was thrilled at his courtesy and warmth which helped the gnawing in my stomach. What a pleasant surprise and difference from our supercilious French officials so puffed-up with their own self-importance. Because I was last and everyone had already passed through, I finished quickly and my two saviors drove me to the hotel that Bill had reserved.

And what a hotel! Small, dark and ugly, it was modest in the extreme, and on the wrong side of the tracks. The old lady at the desk lent an air of propriety. Other denizens of the lobby were also old ladies. What kind of a place was this? They sat in the faded velvet high-backed chairs, gossiping with each other. All abuzz with conjecture, eyes were riveted on me and my passage to the desk where the old lady was joined by another spinster of indeterminate age. At the request of the Travelers' Aid women she took my information and extra money for safekeeping.

"You'll get it all back when you leave, dear," she said.

I signed the register with misgivings. It seemed so strange to see my name, written in my own handwriting, "Mrs. William Thompson," who was she? Perhaps she was an imposter, using my hand to write her name. The hotel called on a large colored woman to carry my luggage up the stairs although I could have done it myself. Mrs. Rice extended her hand and a business card.

"Keep this with you, should you need our help, if you get lost, or want to know anything, we'll be in touch when your flight becomes available." I murmured my thanks but I knew I would not be calling on her anytime soon.

My room offered a large creaky wooden bed, adorned with a wrinkled coverlet, brown ceiling and half an unpainted wall decorated with execrable posters. Down the narrow corridor were a communal toilet and shower which appeared none too clean. I doubted their sanitary arrangements and dreaded having to share them with the other inmates. The whole hotel smelled musty and terribly run down — I was disappointed beyond numbness.

The telephone was in the lobby, one flight below. It was certainly different from the splendiferous image Bill had painted for me of his America. Outside the dingy curtains, snow continued to swirl and the sky at two o'clock was as dark and gloomy as late afternoon. I flung myself spread-eagled on the rickety bed and assessed my situation. I let my mind wander, first to home, North Africa would be swollen with heat right now, I reflected, but resolutely pushed that thought out of my mind.

What if Lola's Stefan never came? I couldn't stop thinking about her and made up my mind to help in whatever way I could.

I knew where the dock was in relation to my hotel and took a chance to see if she was still there. I wished I had better shoes to wear than my morocco ones. Although they were thick, rubber-soled, and quite comfortable, I had been living in them aboard ship all during the storm and they had never dried out completely. Now I had to subject them to snow, yet another trial. I wished for my ski boots but, since the distance was so near, I walked as swiftly as I could, back to the dock.

I prayed it would be empty but there was

Lola, shivering, sitting forlornly on her suitcase, head tucked into her sweater collar, worn out from worry.

"Lola, what do you think happened?" She didn't seem surprised to see me.

"Do you have an address at least?" I asked.

"I have his parents' address, but there's no phone."

"Let's find a cab and go there," I suggested.

She shook her head stubbornly.

"I know he expects to find me here, you don't have to wait if you don't want to. The crew and the first mate offered to help but I didn't want anyone to know that I was afraid. Especially the crew."

Leaving her was out of the question, but so was sitting in the snow. I had a vision of both of us frozen stiff as the day wore into night.

Suddenly she straightened, jumped to her feet and yelled, "Look, look there!" I followed her pointing finger and could barely make out the figure of a man walking briskly, hands thrust deep into his pockets as if on a mission.

"Is it him?" I cried.

"I don't know, Stefan is taller maybe, he doesn't walk like him, I can't tell, he's too far away."

I felt it couldn't be her Stefan as my impression of him was that of a rough man of action; I expected him charging toward us, sweeping her up in his arms, kissing her violently. This man didn't give that impression.

As he neared he called out, "Any trouble, girls?"

We were both speechless with disappointment.

Lola tried to explain, her English words tumbling out over her French.

"Whoa, slow down, I'm not following you. You say he didn't show up?"

"No, he didn't come, my husband, here is card of his address, you know where it is?"

He studied the card and shook his head. I examined him in the fading light. He was young, with dark hair and a black goatee, he seemed all right, but I was nervous anyway.

As if interpreting my thoughts, the young man said, "This is a civilized country, girls, and I don't know where you come from, but nothing can happen to you here. Come on, I'll get you a cab." He picked up the suitcase and we meekly followed. He hailed a taxi, gave the address to the driver and, sticking his head in the open window, wished us good luck. We needed it.

It wasn't far from the docks, probably close to my hotel, also on the wrong side of the tracks, shabby and poor. I took it all in with a glance as I paid the driver and we hauled Lola's suitcase between us up the walk of the little house. Surrounded by old tires, broken toys, odds and ends of detritus, it stood in a small yard, patches of unmelted snow clinging to the protected areas. There were no shrubs, no trees. It was not a welcome addition to Lola's already perilous state. Fortunately she barely noticed. A group of dirty-faced urchins surrounded us as we stopped at the front door.

"Is this the house of Stefan Novinsky?" I asked.

"Yes, he lives here," one of them answered, the others nodded.

Finally Lola pulled herself together, ascended

the small landing, and knocked at the door. She couldn't look at me.

Like a rush of wind, the door flung open and a burly bearded man in a torn shirt, clutching an empty wine bottle, glared at us through red-rimmed eyes.

"Well, what do you want?" he snapped.

Pointing to herself, all pretense of English language gone, Lola stammered, "Me, me, wife, Stefan wife," pointing to her chest with her thumb. He scowled uncomprehendingly and, now to amplify the picture, came the sound of a strident woman's voice nearing the door.

"What, what does she say? Goddamnit that's what we need now, Stefan got no wife." She shook her stringy hair, harsh speech slurred. "Get out, we don't know no wife, Stefan got no wife." Her slatternly haunches were wrapped in a sort of ragged housecoat, "You're not welcome here, we don't know about no wife." I had hung back but now rushed forward to Lola's side.

The drama was unraveling rapidly and I could see Lola's plans of home, children and husband vanish in a puff of smoke. If these were truly his parents, what kind of a man could he be? I realized that Lola's very existence was threatened and that only I could do anything to help her, she was clearly unable to help herself, turned to stone as she appeared to be.

Growling menacingly, the man hurled his bottle at us, and slammed the door in our faces.

She turned to me in despair.

"What am I to do?" she wailed.

The only thing that came to my mind was: "Let's go to the French Consulate."

We dragged her heavy suitcase to the corner where I remembered seeing a phone booth. I called a cab using the tattered telephone directory we found there.

We were silent while we waited. It was cold and getting dark, snow was intermittent.

There was an apparent change in Lola. The blustering howling tiger had given way to a meek little pussycat. Had it not been for my support, I doubt she would have been able to function on her own in those first few hours.

As if reading my mind, she turned to me with a wan smile.

"Thank you for everything, how quick you are to think of what to do, I'm really grateful."

We entered the big imposing building. What a relief to be inside and out of the weather. The fluorescent lights glowed and I felt somewhat cheered. I gripped Lola's arm and whispered, "Don't worry, everything will be all right, you'll see." I wasn't so sure that it would, but had to keep her spirits up.

The consul turned out to be a kind paternalistic man who shook hands with both of us and courteously escorted us to chairs. He asked our permission to smoke, lit up a cigarette, offered the pack to me, I shook my head. Lola took one, and, drawing heavily, seemed to calm down considerably.

"Now what's all this about, ladies?" he asked.

Taking a deep breath, Lola stammered, "I don't know where my husband is." Her voice shook so much she had trouble getting the words out.

"I assume you were married legally?" he inquired gently.

Digging in her bag, she drew out her papers to show him.

"I'm sorry to have to ask that, but you see, my dear, many young women come over here thinking they are brides and it turns out that the marriage was only valid in the country they came from. So please tell me, slowly, what exactly happened."

With some prompting from me, Lola spilled out her story, about how they met, fell in love and married, both in a church and at the city hall in Algiers, how Stefan had mustered out of the army and was discharged, and left for home before she was able to go with him.

Lola said, "He's been here, we even went to his parents' home, they never heard of me, he's been here alone nearly half a year; he couldn't have forgotten all about me, the plans we made, the things we were going to do, the family we wanted." She broke down and sobbed, her head in her hands. The consul and I waited patiently, no one said anything. Only her sobs broke the silence.

"Yes, yes, I'm sorry you've had such a bad time, but I must ask you, do you have any money with you?"

"Why? Is it going to cost me money for your help?" Lola's head shot up, "I have maybe twenty dollars, why do you ask?"

"No, of course not, but if you are indeed stranded, and have no funds, I will have to make some arrangements so that you will have a place to stay while we search for your missing husband."

He was all set to book her into a hotel when I volunteered to have her stay with me.

"It's a big bed, no need for an extra room, besides I'll be glad of the company," I explained. I noticed when I gave him the address that he shook his head mournfully and sighed.

The consul made a lot of notes during Lola's story, took Stefan's serial number, army rank and unit. I felt we were on the right track, but had a nagging sensation that wouldn't go away. What could have happened?

"All right now, I've got all the information I need. I'm really very sorry Mme. Novinsky, we'll do all we can to locate your husband, I want you to be safe in your mind and not worry. Here is some money for dinner and it's good that your friend will be with you, it's less lonely and time will pass quickly. I hope to have some news for you by mid-morning or early afternoon at the latest, so remain at the hotel where I can reach you by phone."

Lola continued on her silent way as we cabbed back to the crummy hotel. She turned to me at one point and whispered, "Manola, what if he's dead?"

"Why would you think the worst right away, for God's sake, probably something happened, but if he was dead, you would know it, I'm sure."

We did not eat particularly well that night, I tried everything in my power to engage her in conversation, but the familiar irreverent Lola was away, perhaps for good.

Neither of us slept soundly, and, no wonder, every time we drifted off, a train would rumble past and jolt us awake. I nearly regretted our quiet nights on board ship with no responsibilities, only our dreams and the thoughts of soon-to-be realized pleasures mixed with the pain, real pain that I carried with me always in the image of my lost son. Except for the storm, that trip had been without obligation, I almost wished myself back where our worst dilemma was not yet realized. And what about our companions in trial, the other girls? Was Lola wishing the same thing? Did Al White know of our plight? Probably not, there would be nothing he could do anyway, but how I longed for his strength and good humor.

Soon the terrible night was over and even with that little sleep we were refreshed.

"I wish I didn't have to put my feet on the floor again," Lola sighed. Clutching her pillow in an agony of defeat of sleep, she tried to avoid getting out of bed.

I urged her to get up and into the communal shower. She was distressed, agitated, wringing her hands, swinging violently between uncontrollable laughter and tears. I had to help her to dress.

I had to call Arlette and let her know about this new development. Because she disliked Lola, and I didn't want to leave her alone, I would have to postpone our breakfast meeting for the following day. Fortunately Lola wanted to stay around the hotel waiting for news as the consul had advised; I elected to wait with her.

"But Manola, my husband arrives sometime tomorrow afternoon, so do come along early so that we can at least get some shopping done."

I was not surprised at this, knowing how selfish Arlette had proven herself to be. She had no compassion at all for Lola.

True to his word the kind consul called mid-morning and requested our presence at his office.

Lola wore a gray woolen dress, the plainest she owned and said, "I feel like I'm going to a funeral."

"You look very nice, come on, let's get going."

We were greeted by a mask-like face; the man was trying to conceal his feelings and my heart plummeted like an out-of-control elevator. Something must be very wrong.

With great solemnity he ushered us to chairs, regained his own seat, and fastened his eyes on the brilliant bouquet of out-of-season flowers artfully arranged on his desk. He had trouble meeting our eyes and, finally, when he looked up, it was to see Lola on the edge of her chair, hands wrapped in each other to still their trembling, silently imploring him on. Her eyes beseeched him to tell her something, anything, so that her nightmare could end.

He riffled through some loose papers in front of him, still having difficulty in meeting Lola's eyes. Finally it came, "I have news about your husband."

He stopped. We both held our breath.

"I'm sorry to say it's not going to be very pleasant news and you may wish you'd never heard it."

He sighed deeply.

As if hurrying to get the unpleasantness behind him, he now rushed ahead. "I'm really very sorry to tell you your husband has been convicted of murder."

There, it was said.

Lola jumped to her feet, her trembling hands clutched at her head, she screamed, "No, no, it's not possible!"

Unable to move, I turned to wood.

The consul rose, rounded the edge of the desk and, gripping her elbow forcibly, pushed her back into her chair.

Her large hands slammed the desk top and she screamed, "How could it happen, it *can't* be true, it *can't* be," and her head dropped to her hands and she sobbed, deep, gut-wrenching sobs.

I didn't want to be part of this. I didn't want to be there. How cruel, how irrational, how unfair. Whatever it was, the dream for her had collapsed inward, had gobbled itself up.

The consul reached for a box of tissues and shoved it across the desk while she continued to deny and moan and shiver.

I finally was able to move. I got up and clutched her firmly around the shoulders and she turned to me and sobbed into my chest, "Why, why, how could this happen, you must be wrong."

This, a direct attack at the consul.

"No, it happened shortly after he arrived home. It's possible his own parents don't even know. He killed another man in a bar fight and there were plenty of witnesses. He'll probably serve a very long time, and I'm sorry to say, my dear, that there is no reason for you to hang around hoping he'll get out in a few years. I've made arrangements to repatriate you, and, as sad as this is, better that you find out now rather than later what type of man you married. I've found you a ship that sails tonight, I'm really very, very sorry to be the bearer of such bad tidings, I'd have preferred a happier outcome."

The poor beleaguered man sighed once again and resumed his study of the floral bouquet.

"The army did this!" Lola shouted, shaking her fist, the short fuse of her temper exploded into invective.

"The damned army made him into a murderer, that's what happened."

"It's possible, my dear, that you may have made a mistake in your choice."

"I don't care, I want to see him, take me to him, I won't believe it until he tells me himself," and she stood up.

"Sit down. I didn't want to have to tell you this, but it looks as if you won't believe it any other way. He was told you'd arrived and he flatly refused to see you. In fact, it was his idea to send you home. Too bad that you never got married in front of the American authorities, at least you'd have recourse. Face it, there's no future for you here."

He sat up straighter in his chair. "Life is a great gamble, my dear young woman, and on this throw of the dice you lost, I am sorry."

I thought of myself in that instant — gamble, yes — I too had gambled on my choice. Would it turn out to be a good one? Once more I was filled with apprehension, but this time for myself.

I whispered, "Go back Lola, go back home."

The consul shot me a grateful look, and, as if in response to both our urging, Lola slowly nodded in assent and mumbled, "All right, I'll go."

I'll never forget the sight of her at the rail, her head high, was she putting on a good face for me? Her body shouted distress signals contrary to those of her head. Occasionally she mopped her eyes with her scarf and at one time shot me a brilliant Lola-type smile. In a loud voice to be heard over the foot traffic she shouted *Mektoub*, what will be will be, and, with stinging eyes, I nodded gravely back. She was gone.

CHAPTER 7

IT WAS TIME to meet Arlette. I'd had the presence of mind to find a cleaner who pressed my gray Paris-before-the-war suit that Arlette had never seen. I knew it was still in style and of course I had a cute gray satin hat, like a turban, hugging my forehead. By the time I was dressed I looked like a dream and knew it from the spin in front of my cracked mirror in the dismal room which still echoed Lola's ghost.

Now hatted, gloved and shod as if to meet a lover, I reveled in the admiring glances of the old lady at the front desk, the cab driver who took me to another finer part of town, and the elegant uniformed doorman who opened my taxi door.

Arlette's accommodations were staggeringly different from mine. I stepped in and gasped at the splendor of the glittering mirrored lobby. The warmth and freshness from the huge potted trees and plants artfully arranged gave off an atmosphere of old money. A costumed bellhop with a pillbox hat directed me to the elevator which whisked me up and up to her suite.

Arlette flung open the door and stepped back, whistling in admiration; her eyes widened when she took me in, my appearance stunning her for a moment.

"Formidable," she gushed, "you're *so* chic!"

Her rooms were filled with the fresh cut flowers her husband had sent to make up for his late arrival, and the ornamental dazzling white drapery at the wide clean windows gave out onto a view of the city. Her white matching satin bedspread and the pink wall-to-wall carpeting were lush and exuded a feeling of luxury. In contrast with my poor *pissoir* down the hall, her private bath and toilet were sparkling with cleanliness. Of course the private telephone was next to the bed from which she dialed room service.

My heart contracted thinking of the sagging deadness of my hotel's curtains and my squeaking old bed. They had nothing in common with her blond Swedish modern furnishings.

Room service delivered yet more flowers and the bottle of champagne Arlette had ordered to celebrate our safe arrival as new American wives. Little did she know how much I appreciated the gesture as my morale was at its lowest ebb, both for myself and Lola. What could Bill be thinking of? Baltimore did have lovely hotels, evidently someone had made an awful mistake.

"Manola, is your hotel nice?"

I refrained from telling her the truth, mainly because I was embarrassed for my husband who may have been responsible for the flea trap I was in.

I steered the conversation toward a middle ground, reluctant to divulge too much of my apprehensions. Fears for Lola's future filled my thoughts while I watched Arlette primp in front of the mirror trying on earring after earring. Her idle chatter, her grandiose plans for herself helped me take my mind off my current problems.

Ready at last, Arlette turned to me, grasped my arm and, swaying slightly from the champagne, we descended to the lobby coffee shop which she assured me was the place for breakfast. She couldn't have been more gracious and charming.

We exclaimed over the long counter that ran the length of the coffee shop. The lighting was spectacular, we glowed under the scintillating tiny crystal prisms dangling from the opulent chandeliers. It was busy and crowded, full of chattering women at both the counter and at each table.

We were shown to a window booth where my attention was caught immediately by the passing parade.

Perhaps because it was a business morning, people were rushing past each other looking neither left nor right, but straight ahead. There was not a stroller nor saunterer to be seen. No one stopped to greet friends or business associates. There seemed to be no interaction between them. Whenever one recognized another, they acknowledged the other's presence with a peculiar gesture, a sort of half-wave, half-salute, sometimes accompanied by a smile and sometimes not.

At first I thought it was because of the cold day and intermittent falling snow, then I reflected on the basic rudeness of what I had observed. No, it couldn't be that, Americans are usually warm and friendly. Why is everyone in such a hurry? I remembered a business day at home in Algiers when two associates would meet in mid-sidewalk.

"How are you, my friend, how is your wife, your mother, your fine children?"

"Ah, thank you, and your health and that of your family, I trust, is well?"

Such niceties were obligatory where I came from, my attention was so riveted to the window in these few seconds that I never even heard Arlette's question.

"Pardon?" I asked.

"Eat, what are we going to eat, Manola, can you read the menu?"

We couldn't quite figure out the menu, some of the items we had heard our husbands talk about, "hamburger", "short stack", we recognized but didn't know what they were. We glanced surreptitiously at the tables near us trying to match up the food we saw with the listed menu. No luck. Then the perky waitress, in her costume of swirling orange apron, lapel flower to match, short turquoise skirt with full petticoats, and a little ruffled hat-type thing on her head, arrived with her pad and pencil.

I pointed to the next table. "What is that?"

"That's a banana split, Madam."

"Good, I'll have one."

"Single or double?"

I looked at Arlette who was openly laughing. "Double?" I asked her.

"Yes of course double, we'll each have one."

It was enormous! A giant boat-shaped glass platter heaped high with ice cream, fruit, whipped cream, chopped nuts, chocolate syrup and a red cherry on the top. We gingerly tasted, then dove in without another word. Absolutely delicious! This was the nectar of the Gods, no wonder our home-sick husbands missed their banana splits. We spooned up the very last drop, sat back, content.

Our cheerful waitress re-appeared and asked, "Anything else, ladies?"

In unison we said, "Yes, bring us another one."

The people at surrounding tables were pointing and laughing. We were the cynosure of all eyes, the two smartly dressed young foreigners busily mopping up yet another American double banana split.

Replete now and a little queasy, to tell the truth, Arlette was full of plans as she pulled out a pack of Players and a monogrammed silver lighter.

"Arlette, I didn't know you smoked".

"On board ship it wasn't allowed, so I forgot about it until now." Perhaps that contributed to her lack of humor and snappish temper. She inhaled deeply and leaned back in the booth, her face a little pale, sweat beading her upper lip.

"I sent Charles a wire the minute we docked, and he called to let me know he's arriving tonight by train. We still have time to do some shopping, what do you say? I need to get some air."

"Yes," I needed air myself, "let's go buy ourselves a little fantasy just to re-light the sacred fire."

It was snowing very heavily and we had no snow boots so had to stay as local as possible. Fortunately her hotel was in the best part of town and the nicest shops were just a step away. Arlette chose a flirtatious polka dot nightie in pink and white with black accents, and I picked out a sexy pair of black lace panties.

"Wait till Bill sees you in those!" Arlette exclaimed and we giggled and laughed together like two old friends.

Back at her hotel Arlette insisted I stay for tea.

We gazed out at the brownstone houses across the street, so different from our white villas at home. The snow continued to fall and Arlette yammered on about whether Charles was going to make her spend another night in this dump.

I was shocked. "Dump?" I said, "you should see my place, if you think this hotel is a dump."

"Well, look about you, the drapes are off color from the rest of the furnishings, and who knows when the carpeting was last cleaned. It's so drab and inelegant, the furniture is old- fashioned, I mean, can't you see it?"

Mrs. know-it-all had re-started one of her favorite diatribes and I tactfully withdrew from the field, but couldn't help a feeling of pity for her poor husband.

"I'll be glad to leave for New York, the awful trip, the terrible arrival and having to submit to being fingerprinted, the questions these people ask, dealing with the luggage, I mean, I am quite worn out with it all."

I smiled. If she had been through what I had faced these past days, she wouldn't have survived, but then, she wouldn't have put herself in the way of receiving the abuse of Stefan's parents, Lola's heart-break, disappointment, and sad departure. She would have cleverly found a way out of that.

I was relieved when a soft knock sounded at the door.

Arlette called, "Come in," and turned expectantly. The door opened and there was Charles. Devoid of his colonel's grand uniform, this was an ordinary man. Slightly overweight, red-nosed, with a bloated face, he was not the imposing figure that Arlette had lauded to the skies. I was surprised. She had led me to believe that he cut an elegant figure, I imagined him as slender as a sword blade, graceful and romantic.

He dropped his small suitcase and, charging forward like a runaway bus, grasped her in his arms and kissed her passionately. I looked away.

"For God's sake, is *that* the only coat you own? You look like a beggar."

I cleared my throat, wishing I was not there.

"And who is *this*?" the man inquired coming toward me, ignoring his wife's insult.

"Oh, that's Manola, another bride, one of the girls from the boat."

Arlette turned to powder her nose. There was a decided chill in the air and I wondered how her lovely new polka dotted confection would survive this first night together with the husband she hadn't bargained for. I imagined his impatience in trying to rip it off, after hurling her onto the bed and rolling on top of her, roaring in excitement, trying to press his lips to every appropriate place on her body. And then what? How would Arlette react? Would she sigh, then give in gracefully, or would she put aside her misgivings and respond in kind? Who knows.

Charles bent over my outstretched hand with both of his enormous red paws, and I had a sensation of being engulfed by a bear of a man who smelled slightly of what I took to be mutton fat. He then gently kissed my cheek and smiled vaguely.

I felt for him, he didn't deserve the rude unwelcoming reception he received from his beloved wife and I regretted being there to see it.

It was time for me to leave. I kissed Arlette goodbye and hugged her. She wouldn't meet my eyes. Her disenchantment was as palpable as Lola's scream had been, and I wondered, "If three's the charm, am I going to suffer a disappointment like theirs?"

Now I was alone, truly alone. It was still snowing, I slipped and slid on the sidewalk leading to the Greyhound bus terminal where the Travelers' Aid people had told me to eat. With boots and a better sense of direction, and, had it not been constantly snowing, I would have ventured further afield, but I was nervous about getting wet and lost.

As it was with the menu in Arlette's hotel coffee shop, I could puzzle out the items but had a devil of a time pronouncing their names. The waitress would double up laughing whenever I would look over at someone else's plate and say, "Give me the same".

The other waitresses would linger nearby to hear me attempt to order, compare notes and try to mimic my accent. They said, "It was c-u-u-t-e".

I became a celebrity with some of the regulars who were told I was a French newcomer, a war bride, and could have made friends with some of them had I wished. I didn't wish, being shy and rather used to formality in my associations. I did get to see the same bus drivers over and over, as they deposited their passengers, ate, picked up a new load, then took off again.

This went on for days and days. I nearly lost count, but the snowstorm never seemed to end, and until it did, my flight could not take off.

I tried to practice my English on the little old ladies who made up the hotel guests, but was constantly frustrated at not being able to understand. I did not realize that they were from the deep South and their way of speaking, as well as their accent, was not the English I had learned in school. I later found out that their speech patterns and choice of words were just as incomprehensible to other Americans as they were to me.

The hotel maid also baffled me, but for other reasons. She was as black as ebony and her smiling, cheerful face, full of white teeth, brightened my every day when she showed up to clean my room. She was middle-aged and heavy, and there was something about her so maternal, I became home-sick. She was kind and caring, and I wanted to become a child again, crawl into her lap, cradle my head against her capacious bosom and tell her all my fears and secrets.

I did all the talking in this relationship. I followed her about the room, and even out into the hallway as she mopped the common bathroom, talking, always talking. She didn't have much to answer, but I felt as close to her as anyone I had yet met in this country.

"I want you to sign my travel diary," I announced one day when she was getting ready to leave.

"Oh no, honey, you sure don't want me to write in your pretty book," she protested.

"Oh but I do, you're the first friend I made here in the United States, and I really do want to have your signature right here on this page. Here's the pen, come on, sign your name."

Slowly the maid wrote her name, Ruth, in my book as I held it steady, she filled the last page. I planned to mail it to Jean-Pierre, my son, before I left Baltimore.

Hugging her around the shoulders, I was astonished to see big tears creeping down the polished cheeks of the face so close to my own. I exclaimed, "What's the matter? Surely writing your name in my book shouldn't make you cry?"

Her beautiful eyes awoke all the tenderness in me and I kissed the wet cheeks. "What's the matter, have I said something to offend you?"

The streaming eyes looked deep into mine and a choking voice replied, "You don't understand, do you?"

She ran across the room and out the door

before I could react to stop her.

The next day when I tried to talk her into accompanying me on a little shopping spree, followed by lunch together, she was sorrowful.

"Baby, you don't understand, you gonna have to learn that here ain't like where ya'll come from. Negro folks just don't mix with white folks. Colored folks ain't allowed in white folks' restaurants, colored folks ain't allowed to mix. You go ask those white ladies sittin' in the lobby, they'll tell you how it is."

I did exactly that. I picked one of the hotel denizens that spent her days in the same chair in the lobby, tentatively approached her and told her my problem.

She was aghast.

"But, child, you mustn't do things like that. It's God's blessing that you ran into a nice sensible colored that knows her place. If it was one of them uppity gals from up North, you might have bought yourself a heap of trouble."

She called over several other old ladies who confirmed with agitated shaking of heads and tsk-tsking the taboo which I had nearly broken. They treated me to a lecture cum tirade for over an hour on the place of colored people in white society.

When they made their way up to their beds, one by one, I realized I was not alone in the lobby.

The young man sitting in the chair nearby was smiling. I knew his face because I had seen him in uniform at the Greyhound restaurant.

"I couldn't help hearing what those old biddies were telling you," he laughed. "I'm a Northerner, so perhaps I don't feel the way these rebels do, but let me tell you that colored people have a rougher time of it here in the South because the whites won't let it be forgotten that the Africans were once their slaves, their property. Where I live, up North, both races can send their kids to the same school, colored and white work and live side by side in relative neighborliness, the colored can shop where they like and eat almost where they choose. We have colored doctors and lawyers, for God's sake. These people down here are still living in their glorious past. Some day it may change, but it'll take a long time, generations perhaps. So of course you can't invite the maid to lunch. My dear, what an idea." He mimicked the tone and attitude of the old lady to perfection and I laughed in spite of myself.

He was outgoing, engaging, warm and friendly, the way most Americans had proved to be. His lanky form clad in bus driver gray, his long face spreading into lines of humor, I found chatting with him easy perhaps because he didn't criticize me the way the old ladies had.

"So tell me, what've you seen of our glorious country?" he asked.

"What, me, nothing at all," I replied. "I'm waiting for the weather to clear and a seat on the plane to the West Coast where I'll be living."

"You mean you haven't seen anything but the lobby of this crummy hotel and the lavish restaurant at the terminal where I see you eating every day?"

I hadn't realized he recognized me, but then knew I was the butt of the waitresses' jokes so he knew all about me, certainly more than I would have preferred a stranger to know.

"Look, I think it's terrible a girl like you should be cooped up in your hotel room day after day when there's a big world out there to be discovered."

"Oh sure, I'd love to discover the big world," I replied soberly, "but I'm afraid to get lost, which is why I eat every meal in the same place. You see, my English is not very good yet and I'm really frightened to lose my way in this strange city."

"Oh kid, I don't suppose you thought you might write the hotel's name and address and phone number on a piece of paper to show a passing cab driver so he'd know where to bring you home?"

I admitted the idea had merit, but it had never crossed my mind.

We talked about this and that, he asked me about Algeria and appeared to listen with great interest. He was enthusiastic about his country and warmed to his subject when talking about his travels and sightseeing and all the places he'd been in the United States. I confessed that I too would like to see some of them.

"After all, I'll be seeing all of America soon, but from the air," I said.

"That doesn't count," he scoffed. "The way to see the country is by road. By bus for example."

Suddenly he leaned over and grasped my arm in that overly familiar way Americans have and exclaimed, "I've got it, why don't you come with me to Philadelphia tomorrow?"

"What's Philadelphia," I asked, trying to imitate his pronunciation.

"The birthplace of democracy, that's what. Where the Declaration of Independence was signed. You know, 4th of July? Bang, bang."

I shook my head. His words were confusing and I was getting tired. Whenever I got tired, I couldn't listen to English any more.

120

"Never mind, here's my plan. I have to take a 9:00 A.M. trip up North, to deliver a bunch of service men to their mustering out point at a separation center near Harrisburg called Indian Town Gap. Getting there takes about three hours, a little less. You come with me, and you'll get to see the country in the spacious comfort of a Greyhound bus. Then we'll proceed onto Philadelphia where I'll stay, and you go sightsee, eat, then take any Greyhound back home, they leave every hour and you can afford the fare, it's only a few dollars. What do you say?"

"What would I do there?"

"Well, you'll get to see Philadelphia. You can see the Liberty Bell, Independence Hall, Ben Franklin's house, lots of things."

"Sounds interesting, and I'm so bored sitting here in between meals, just waiting to go eat, perhaps I'll come," but then I hesitated.

"What's wrong?"

"My shoes, I don't really have the right shoes to walk long distances, that's another reason I don't go out much, it's been too wet and my feet are always cold and damp because my shoes let the water in."

He laughed. "Oh don't worry, it'll be dry there, it's a totally different city and it's in the North, not like here in the South at all. You simply have to see the North before you go out West."

That clinched it for me. The waitresses and even the cashier at the terminal restaurant had been teasing me unmercifully about my short round trips three times daily.

"From the hotel to eat, back to the hotel, what a life you're living," they had said. "Get out and see something of the city, Baltimore is really very nice when you go to the good part of town."

I knew that already, but I was too shy and still too uncomfortable with the language to take any of their suggestions. Now I'd show them.

What to wear for a trip on a big bus with a bunch of young servicemen? I had seen those buses in the terminal belching like giant horses restive in their stalls. I decided on a pleated plaid skirt in dark purple and yellow that had a matching yellow angora pullover. I looked very girlish and young. Of course I had my trusty white coat which was getting dingier by the day. I looked closely at my rubber-soled Morocco shoes. They too were fading fast, but they were all I had and would have to do.

Lines of people were forming under the high roof of the terminal. The noise and smell were overpowering. I looked left and right for Bob, which was the name he had given me, and almost immediately spotted him standing on the elevated step of a bus apart from the others, also looking left and right, presumably for me.

We waved at each other and I made my way over there. He helped me up the high step and into the seat directly behind him.

I blushed at the multitude of wolf whistles and teasing remarks addressed to the "lucky driver" but Bob ignored them and suddenly, as if in response to some secret signal, the pneumatic doors swung shut, closing out the noise of the terminal, and the giant craft eased out into the street. My big adventure had begun and I settled back fully expecting to enjoy every minute.

The skies were gray and it was bitterly cold and snowy, giving me pause. I couldn't walk very far in weather like this here in Baltimore and presumably it would be colder in the Northern city of Philadelphia — I gave up trying to say it to myself, but for now it was warm and comfortable in the bus and I thoroughly enjoyed the passing panorama of the countryside.

This was new to me. The tidy farms with their rectangles of fields coated in snow, the snug houses dwarfed by the tremendous barns, the glimpses of people and animals moving about the outbuildings, and the children playing in the snow. What impressed me most was the number of creeks and small rivers over which we passed, the bus rolling along silently.

Accustomed to the arid moonscape of North Africa, so much water was a marvel. I could imagine how green and lush it would be in the spring and I envied the farmers their richness of water, what would it be like I wondered, when all the snow would melt, swelling the creeks and overflowing the small stream beds.

The trees hung heavy with damp snow, the world was a silent wonder. Not a palm tree to be seen, I smiled to myself at that.

Good for me to be going to California where palms were plentiful, or so I had been told. Also the sun, my ally and savior. I had not seen his face yet in this gray country. I imagined I'd have to be in California before the sun would come to me.

The drone of the soldiers talking and singing and making noise faded into the background and I was able to tune them out.

As the miles unrolled and the hours flew by, I felt full of myself, quite the world traveler, I thought.

I was so elated that I had been talked into this trip and grateful to the gum-chewing silent Bob in front of me who piloted his vehicle with skill and precision, never taking his eyes from the road.

Just as he promised, about three hours and a quarter into the trip, he turned the big bus off the main highway onto a smaller secondary road. With a hiss of the great brakes, the bus ground to a stop in front of a guard post flanking a large gated entrance. I scrambled to straighten out my legs curled under my skirt before the boys disembarked. I pulled it down into position and sat up. I could only make out the closest buildings as the doors swung open and one by one with coarse remarks to no one in particular, the noisy soldiers clattered off. I was glad I didn't really understand what they were saying. They were a happy lot, all getting ready to return to civilian life.

After the boys left, peace and quiet descended, the mighty steed swung into high gear once again on the secondary road and thence onto the highway. As we were alone, I sat forward in my seat propping my head up on my hands, elbows on the back of Bob's driver's chair. I couldn't hear what he had to say otherwise and I wanted him to know how grateful I was for this outing, and how much I appreciated his suggesting it. We rolled happily along the countryside again and some more time passed before we neared the city. I could see tall buildings and, when I asked, Bob affirmed that, yes, we were going to be coming into Philadelphia soon. We were on the outskirts now and I saw small filling stations, little neighborhood food stores, and what looked like small factories.

"Like all big city environs, this is just as depressing as Baltimore," Bob said, reading my mind. I was too polite to offer this opinion first.

"Of course, our terminal is never situated in the finest part of town either, so be prepared, it won't be a pretty sight."

"You promised me the weather would be better here," I pouted.

"True, I thought it would be clearer, but it seems to be snowing just as hard in Philadelphia as in Baltimore, but so what, we'll have fun anyway, even here where nothing ever happens."

He had a report to file, and I was well into my second cup of coffee, wondering what the difference was between one bus terminal lunch counter in one city or another, they looked identical, when Bob slid onto the stool next to mine.

"Gee, I'm sorry kid, it's really coming down too hard for you to use these, but I picked them up for you anyway," and he slipped some brochures outlining the delights of Philadelphia's charms under my elbow. I was touched by his thoughtfulness but knew that, in all practicality, I couldn't go sightseeing with my leaky shoes and the heavy snow.

"What shall I do then?" I asked.

"Tell you what, stick with me, O.K.? I just got word that I have to make an unscheduled run out to yet another demobilization center to pick up some guys and bring them back into town. Come with me, at least you'll be warm and dry and out of the weather, and it'll kill an hour or two and you can see more of the country. Then I can bring you back here and you can catch a movie, I'll show you where. When you get out, it'll be dinner time, then after you eat, you can take whatever bus home you like, just remember they leave for Baltimore every hour on the hour so if you miss one you have to wait."

He flashed his white toothy grin and was so earnest, I gave in. It was snowing and the thought of the warm bus seemed like a safe haven.

Nervously he glanced around and lowered his voice.

"Tell you what, though, I shouldn't be carrying a passenger, going out from Baltimore with a full load, no one would have noticed, but on an empty bus someone might see you. Would you mind walking straight out the door, turn right at the corner and wait on the opposite side of the street for me? Give me a few minutes head start, O.K.?" Again with the charming smile, of course I did as he asked.

As I jumped on the still moving bus, this time under my own steam, he slammed the door and rammed the throttle. The bus careened around the corner and I was flung into the seat directly behind him. His jaw was set and his horsey face had become grim and cold.

We didn't speak for the first fifteen minutes or so, I was struck by his nervous hurry and wondered the reason for it.

He turned off the main streets again into the outskirts and we left the city behind as he pushed the bus to what seemed like an unsafe speed. I was starting to get a little anxious.

"Where are we going in such a hurry?" I asked, my voice high pitched and childlike.

"I don't want to be late," he replied. I think I made a wrong turn back there, let's try this way," and he maneuvered the big bus onto a narrow lane which led steadily up and up a deserted hilly ridge.

The snow was falling heavily, there was no noise and it was growing darker by the minute. I watched the little muscle at the side of his jaw clench and unclench and noted beads of perspiration cascading down his cheeks. His arm muscles seemed to take on the hardness of iron and were knotted, as he tried to turn the steering wheel.

Suddenly the engine cut off and the bus lurched to a standstill.

"What is happening, where are we, what are you doing?" I protested, my voice growing thinner and weaker. His formerly friendly face had taken on a sinister aspect and as he lunged from his driver's seat at me, I felt I was being attacked by an out of control horse, so large and ominous did his face loom over mine.

"Come on baby," he panted in excitement. "You French babes are all hot for it, come on, I know you want it."

I was strong for my small size and I fought like a tiger, using nails and teeth, feet and fists, some of my blows must have connected with some of his tender parts as he slowed down a little. The bus pitched and rolled almost as badly as the *Bald Eagle*. I was aware of inky dark clouds outside my window as I used every ounce of strength to beat him off. He must have somehow opened his uniform's pants with one hand as he tried to pull my underwear off with the other, using his weight, rangy though he was, to hold me down. I would not be held down.

"You bastard," I screamed at him in French, "you son of a bitch." My English wasn't really up to the curses and my voice was pitched higher than in real life. I knew there was no one around to save me. My language must have excited him still further or perhaps he had been deprived for a long time, because without warning he gave a giant convulsive heave and discharged his weapon all over my beautiful plaid skirt. On and on it poured, as he groaned and bucked, and I was torn between relief that only my skirt was ruined, and fury that this thing could happen to me, and indeed could have been worse.

The wind whipped the snow which in turn beat the trees into submission.

Over, it was over.

My face and sweater were covered in his blood and sweat, but I pushed him off and, running to the door, swung it open and jumped out into the snow.

It was cold, my breath condensed forming white clouds of mist and I breathed heavily, drawing the freezing air into my laboring lungs. I couldn't stop sobbing or trembling, partly from cold but mostly from this devastating betrayal.

There was silence for many minutes, eventually he must have closed his pants, pulled himself together, regained his seat, and now, calm and at ease again, turned the engine over to re-start the bus.

Was he going to leave me here? How would I get back to any type of civilization? I looked around — nothing. No farms, no people, nothing but a little rabbit which hopped over the snow, turning once to look at me, this foreigner in a foreign land.

"Come on, let's go," he called out.

I hesitated. If I got back on the bus, would there be a repeat performance? How long would it take him to re-load?

"Come on, I'll drop you in Philadelphia."

I had no choice. I boarded the bus.

I was shaking and huddled into my coat, burrowing my way into the farthest corner of the seat, two rows behind him. I managed to bring my sobbing under control.

For his part, he spoke not a word, he used all his concentration to maneuver the bus back down the ridge, angrily.

He hadn't got what he wanted, but at least he wasn't going to leave me to freeze in the snow.

We arrived at our destination without another word. Silently he stopped the bus where he had picked me up, opened the door and waited for me to get off. The last I saw of him was the bus turning the corner, back to the terminal yards.

He hadn't told me where the movie was and I desperately wanted to clean up; I ran for the ladies' room where I effected whatever repairs I could with the crumbling paper towels and liquid soap. My knees were still shaking and I was sore all over from my ordeal.

It was quite dark when I finally emerged from the terminal, the street lights and neon signs had come on. I walked a block or two, when I saw a brightly lighted movie theater. What luck! They were showing Spencer Tracy in *Death of a Salesman*; without a second thought, I bought a ticket, went in and collapsed into a seat.

I must have dozed off, or otherwise lost interest because I dropped the thread of the story. The warmth and darkness did their work and, when I came to, it was to the sound of a Movietone Newsreel. People were getting up and leaving, but I stayed where I was.

I wanted to see the movie and, this time, after the cartoon which somewhat lifted my spirits, I sat through it again.

By the time it was finally finished, and I

must admit I didn't understand a lot of what went on, my stomach was rumbling its protests that it had had nothing since lunch, a long time and much effort ago.

Gathering my coat around me, I set out for the bus terminal, but must have made a wrong turn somewhere because within the two blocks I remembered leaving it, it had disappeared from view.

All the guideposts and landmarks which I thought I remembered from the late afternoon and early evening looked completely different.

The streets were bewilderingly the same. I wandered through the snow, desperately searching for a cab, a policeman, or someone to guide me.

There was no one. I was cold, wet, hungry and, the more I walked, the more tired and exhausted I became. I was as frightened by this experience as the one on the bus, the only difference being that on the bus I wasn't cold, wet or hungry.

Teeth chattering, like an automaton, I plodded forward. Was I alone on this god-forsaken planet? Why were there no people? Why were the streets so deserted? No cars, no foot traffic, no noise, only the intermittent snow which fell silently and the scrunch of my soaking wet and falling-apart shoes.

Even the buildings were forbiddingly dark. Perhaps there had been a power failure. I was so cold and miserable I was numb. The only thing I knew was that day would break and someone would find me frozen to death in my dingy white coat.

After turning a corner, perhaps the same one, I lost count, up ahead I saw a brightness lightening the dark. I picked up my pace, hurrying as best my frozen feet would allow. I was drawn like a moth to a flame. Nearing, I saw that it emanated from neon signs burning madly in a street that seemed to contain all the light that was missing from the rest of the world.

Red, green, yellow, blue, and harsh white messages screamed their wares to the passersby. They hung over the street, crawled up the sides of buildings, dazzling, sparkling, changing every second. I stopped for a moment, struck by the lively scene. It took just that moment to realize I could not stand still there for long. The motley mass of people were almost all uniformed men, or so it appeared at first glance, and the signs and gaiety pointed to bars, night clubs, cheap restaurants, and coffee shops. I strode onward, eyes straight ahead, determined to find a policeman or someone in authority who could help.

Coming towards me on the same side of the street was a tall young man in sailor's knit cap and pea coat. A duffel bag was slung over one shoulder and he stalked purposefully. Had I not stopped him he would have passed me by without a glance.

Because my instinct had not been working well lately, I observed him closely. The one thing he had in his favor, besides his blond open freshness, was that he appeared to be sober. I decided to take a chance.

As he drew near to pass me, I put out a restraining hand.

"Pardon me, could you help me, please?"

Suspiciously he looked me over, no doubt my blue and frozen face allayed any fears that I was accosting him for sex or a handout.

"I can try, what's the trouble, cookie?"

Stumbling over my words, the story, part of it that I could tell, fell out, tumbled over one another making me sound more foreign than ever.

"I'm so lost, the movie let out and I tried to get back to the bus station, but I can't find it, I've been walking around and around for hours and hours, please tell me, where's the bus?"

"Which bus station do you want?" he asked, smiling.

"The Greyhound, I have to get back to Baltimore."

"Well, you're in luck. If you'd just kept going, you'd have run into it eventually. I bet you just went around in circles, getting farther and farther away the whole time. You poor kid, where's home, Baltimore? Not with that accent, I'll bet."

I felt a warning sign. I hated familiarity on first meeting, but all Americans seemed to be like that, so I gave a inward shrug and confessed my situation as a newly arrived war bride waiting to join her husband in California.

"Pretty grim, you're being here in Philly in the midst of the worst snowstorm of the century. What's your name?"

Reluctantly I told him, shifting from one foot to the other.

"I'm sorry," he said, "my name's Jeff. Let's try to get you straightened out. First of all, take my arm and let's get off the strip. This street is not known to be kind to foreign young ladies. He offered his arm and, with a hesitation that he must have felt, I took it.

We walked rapidly away from the bright lights, he tried to adjust his gait so that I could keep up. I asked again. "Is this the way to the station?"

"Yes, but your little blue face tells me you haven't eaten a thing since you got lost, am I right?"

"I'm starving," I confessed. "Lunch was a long time ago."

"If you'll permit me," he asked in a very formal tone, "I know a restaurant that has the best seafood in town. That is, if you haven't eaten enough soft shelled crabs in Baltimore."

"I eat all my meals in the Greyhound bus terminal," I replied. "And they don't have soft shelled crabs. I've had them in Paris and they're very good, so I don't see how Philadelphia could do any better, although I am willing to try."

In this manner, bantering back and forth, Jeff the sailor escorted me to a real restaurant where I was pointed to the ladies' room to make repairs to my ravaged face and hair. The pinched blue nose that stared back at me from the mirror was laughable. I immediately realized that the young sailor must have known my story was genuine, because no lady of the night ever looked as bad as I did at that point. Judicious use of a comb, lipstick and compact fixed the damages and I emerged a new woman.

He had nice manners and rose from the table, admiring. I had seen that look before and determined to maintain my reserve so that he wouldn't have the same impression I must have given the bus driver.

The restaurant smelled delicious and my mouth watered. I let him order, and we gorged ourselves on oysters, soft shelled crabs and a giant lobster apiece. I ate ravenously; we barely stopped for conversation. Whenever we did talk in between the clearing of one course to the next, I found him to be witty, fairly well traveled as many sailors are, and I was happy to see that he had some knowledge of French. He teased me gently over my mis-pronunciation of English words and I sputtered with laughter over his imitation of me trying to sound American.

I sopped up the last bit of melted butter with my last piece of bread, wiped my fingers and my mouth, sat back in my chair and resisted the temptation to do as my Arab neighbors at home, belch loudly in appreciation of the food and say *ramdoullah*. He mistook my smile for something else and both of us spontaneously broke into laughter.

"Please excuse my greediness," I patted my rounded belly. "That was *magnifique*, it was so good I couldn't stop."

"Lady, don't apologize. I love a woman with a good appetite. I hate to see anyone pick politely at their plate. I enjoy good food and am happy to have good company to enjoy it with."

I leaned across the table and grasped his hand.

"Thank you for rescuing me, and thank you for the superb meal. I've had a terrible day and this is the first pleasant thing that has happened to me. Do you treat everyone you meet as nicely?" I asked innocently. I didn't want him to think that he was going to go anywhere with this relationship.

He blushed. How lucky I was to have run into him instead of another Bob, but I wasn't going to be duped like that ever again.

I glanced at my watch. It was getting late, I knew the bus for Baltimore left every hour on the hour, and didn't want to run the risk of crossing Bob's path.

Jeff called for the check, and once outside raised his hand for a cab which miraculously appeared.

"It's not very far to the terminal but you look done in, and you've walked enough for one day," he explained.

He took me right up to the ticket window, insisted upon paying for my ticket, and then, very ceremoniously, escorted me onto the waiting bus.

I don't know what time it was when I squished my way into the hotel lobby. It was empty except for the two old ladies at the desk. They looked me over, then, eyebrows raised, turned to each other.

We all began to talk at the same time.

"We were so worried about you we called the police," one of them exclaimed.

"Where were you, what happened?" demanded the other.

"I went to Philadelphia and I got lost there," I replied as calmly as I could and held out my hand for the room key.

I could tell they didn't believe me by the way they looked at each other and nodded. Perhaps they smelled the good meal I had enjoyed, certainly, they could see how wet my shoes were and how tired I looked.

"But they're looking for you," protested the younger one.

"Who's looking for me?"

"The Travelers' Aid people, here's the first of the telephone messages, they have a flight for the West Coast for you tomorrow, and if you hadn't shown up, you'd have lost it."

"Yes, imagine your husband meeting the plane, and you not on it?" sniffed the older one.

"I'm very sorry to have caused you concern, but here I am, and I'll not miss my plane nor my husband," I answered, heading for the stairs. I was exhausted and only wanted to fling myself into bed.

Before doing so I had to wash off the events of the day. I folded my big towel into a small pad in order to step into the stall shower. I always kept a close eye out for vermin, and, although I never saw any, on my last night, I wouldn't have been surprised if an army of roaches, water bugs or rats had emerged from the drains to devour me.

Bad luck breeds bad luck.

Mrs. Rice from Travelers' Aid showed up to take me to the airport.

"I'm sorry, we had to book you via Washington, D.C., there wasn't a direct flight."

I didn't care.

The snow had let up, she gave me back the money left in keeping of the hotel desk, piled me and my luggage into a taxi and took off for the airport.

In spite of my protests, she insisted upon accompanying me, no doubt she was afraid I would get lost again, the old biddies at the hotel must have told her about my escapade.

At the airport, she ensconced me in a chair, disappeared a moment but was back, loading me up with magazines, gum and candy, none of which I wanted.

My flight was called.

"Now listen," she said, taking both my hands and looking me right in the eyes, "don't get lost again, please. You'll be told where to change planes and you'll be on your way to Los Angeles before you know it, and I wish you the best of luck."

She was nice after all, but I knew I wouldn't give her another thought, nor the hotel, nor the experiences I'd had there. I just wanted to forget.

Contrary to expectations, I didn't get lost

again, the transfer from Baltimore to Washington was without incident, but, as usual, my foreign sound caused the cab driver to turn around in his seat and ask, "First time here, honey?"

"Yes, I'm going to California, so I need the other plane terminal."

"Yes, of course, I know that. But if you've never seen Washington, I wouldn't be a good American if I didn't let you visit at least one monument."

Here we go again, just another ruse to keep the meter running and educate a stranger.

He insisted upon taking me past the Lincoln Memorial which under normal circumstances would have been imposing. I didn't really pay much attention as all my focus was on the ticking meter. I never even got out of the cab. I was so suspicious I even worried he would drive away with my luggage, leaving me stranded. I only wanted to get to California.

CHAPTER 8

THE CROSS-COUNTRY FLIGHT was uneventful. I had a window seat, probably thanks to Mrs. Rice, and at first glued my nose to the glass to see what there was to see. Nothing, just clouds and more clouds. I ate the lunch I was brought, I tried to read the magazines, poring over the lush ads in an equal mixture of admiration and heavy scorn. If one were to believe it, any man or, for that matter, any woman would be irresistible to the opposite sex if they used the pictured product. The amounts of money spent to sell shaving cream, muscle building courses, make-up and hair goods, toothpaste and mouthwash must be staggering. I was a little contemptuous of this American mentality, oh well, I'd soon enough be just like them. I dozed. When finally the announcement came that we were approaching Los Angeles, I roused myself to look again and was daunted by the vast sprawl of the city below. I powdered my face, renewed my lipstick, took a deep breath, and prayed for strength.

I followed my fellow passengers off the flight across a stretch of concrete runway, where we were herded through a long echoing tunnel which emptied us into a noisy bright waiting room. I scanned the faces, and re-scanned. At first I didn't recognize Bill.

In the back, standing on the edge of the crowd, was my husband. I didn't want to believe it. I walked toward him and then passed and kept on walking. My mind was in a turmoil. What could I do? Where could I go now? The vision that had filled my eyes these many months had been of a tanned and smiling Bill, blond, almost white, wavy hair blowing in the breeze. I loved his hair.

I know the adage "clothes make the man" and yes, perhaps I'd fallen in love with a uniform, but this creature that allowed me to walk past him was wearing a horrible suit in an unfortunate shade of brown with wide black stripes. His shoulders were exaggerated, the wide coat fell in folds to his knees, the trousers, baggy at the top, tapered to narrow, narrow cuffs at the ankle. With this ridiculous outfit he wore two-toned brown and white shoes. His necktie was loud and his once beautiful hair was plastered to his scalp with some kind of oily pomade. I took this all in in an instant.

It may have been the last word in men's fashions for 1946, but I was appalled by his cheap looks, just like a gangster in the movies.

I passed him by, but was brought up short by his cry.

"*M'amie!*"

Hearing this familiar nickname, I stopped in my tracks, turned around.

His eyes caught mine, and with a broad smile he pushed his way through the crowd.

He swept me into his arms and his welcoming kiss almost made me forget the qualms his appearance had given me. Thank goodness I didn't echo Arlette greeting her Charles.

We picked up my luggage at the carousel. He was strangely quiet and subdued in direct contrast to his loud clothes. I was quiet too, shocked and filled with new fears for my own future.

This Bill was not the confident and charming Bill of our North African days. There he had exuded a sunny air of self-worth, always laughing and clowning around, people loved him he was so cheerful. His face now in repose was set and hard. And when had that line appeared between his eyebrows? He looked worried and upset — could I be the cause? Well, I wouldn't add to whatever burden he was carrying. I resolutely shut my mouth and vowed not to ask him questions. Let's flow with it, I thought, there's nothing I can do about it anyway.

We set off across the enormous parking lot where we encountered his car. This was the icing on the cake. The general dilapidation and advanced age of this steed was just one more indication of Bill's fortune, or lack of it.

He piled my baggage in the back seat, explaining that the trunk's lock was broken.

He helped me into the front seat; its upholstery was ripped, and as he crossed around to get in on the driver's side, I saw his shoulders slump. What could be wrong?

He fiddled with the ignition key, the gas, swore softly under his breath and eventually the engine turned over. I was even more self-conscious when it backfired loudly, coughed a few times, spewed out a plume of smoke from the tailpipe. People laughed at us as he managed to get that wreck of a car under way.

Bill was unperturbed and, with practiced ease, guided the car into the stream of traffic leaving the airport. The engine warmed up, and, after a time, except for an occasional misfired belch, the rattling of something loose under the hood, and a general noise level that made conversation difficult, I'd have almost enjoyed my first ride into Los Angeles.

Bill was a poor guide; he answered my excited queries only with monosyllables or grunts, leaving me to lapse into silence. This balmy air was a far cry from the gloomy and freezing Baltimore I had just left and I reveled in the feeling of well-being. The large houses along Sunset Blvd. were mostly white, with high walls, and gates through which I tried to snatch a glimpse of the interior gardens. He was driving too fast for me to really see anything and I hesitated to ask him to slow down — perhaps the car wouldn't tolerate a more leisurely pace.

What I saw I liked. I could be happy here. I leaned my head on Bill's bulky shoulder and rubbed my cheek on his over-sized pads. He smiled down at me indulgently.

"This is Beverly Hills, babe, and we're on our way to dinner where my friends are looking forward to meeting you."

"But I can't go looking like this, I've been traveling all day in the same clothes, I'd like to change. Can't we stop somewhere first?"

"It's not necessary, you look fine, they know you've been on a plane, don't worry."

With the studied ability of someone who follows a familiar path, Bill swung the car into a side street shaded with tall trees. Lovely shrubbery lined the street and I noticed the cast iron statues of little black jockeys in front of some of the houses.

"What are those for?"

"Those are for holding your horse, if you had one," he laughed. "If you don't want to use a house number, you got one of these little guys painted in

your stable colors, if you had a stable, and if you did-
n't, you just chose some colors that were appealing
to you and ordered your jockey for your driveway
curb. It helps to locate the house you want, especially on a dark night when it's impossible to read
the house number."

Bill squeezed my hand.

I noticed the street sign, "Alpine Drive". I
knew we must be getting near.

Bill turned into a driveway and my heart
stood still. This was the address I had been using to
write him since our separation. Could this lovely
house be ours? It was two story, red brick, solid
looking. He stopped the car at the end of the driveway, slid out and came around to my side.

Silently, he retrieved my luggage and escorted me up the steps to the front door. It was opened
by a smartly dressed maid and almost immediately
we were engulfed by a mob of people.

In the lead was a tall, good-looking man who
threw his arms around me and lifted me off the floor
in an alcoholic bear hug. "How nice to know you at
last, darling, I'm Richard." He was followed by a tall
slim red-haired woman in a hot pink dress, who
opened her arms wide, then clasped me to her
bosom. Geniality flowed from both of them, I felt
confused but welcome.

She released me, stepped back, held me at
arm's length and looked me over long and clearly.
"I'm Diane," and turning toward Bill, "no wonder
you were worried, you should be happy to get her
here finally." Bill loomed in the background,
attempting to make introductions and I was once
again struck by the genuine warmth of these
Americans who didn't know me but greeted me like

a member of their own family. Nothing in my experience had prepared me for this and I was at a loss as to how to behave.

Each of them grasped one of my hands and pulled me along. I held back. "Wait, wait, please, I'd really like to use the bathroom, if you don't mind."

"You want to refresh yourself, Manola?" asked Diane.

"Oh yes, please." She took my suitcase and I followed her upstairs where I washed, changed into a dress, fixed my make-up and re-combed my hair. I was impressed by the lovely silver dressing set, the towels laid out in the bath. I looked and felt much, much better when I descended to rejoin my hosts.

This house was definitely the home Bill had described when we were together in Algeria. But a sinking feeling told me we didn't own this house, I was nothing more than a guest here. I felt it, and wondered what kind of a prank Bill was playing in allowing me to think this was ours. I would rather have gone to whatever little place he had, just to be alone with him.

I entered an arched doorway into the tremendous living room whose focal point was a glistening crystal chandelier.

All turned toward me. There was a moment of silent, I hoped, appreciation, and a fat man struggled out of a chair that appeared several sizes too small for him. He looked very familiar, although I knew we had never met. He made me a courtly bow and Diane gestured toward him.

"Meet Charles Laughton."

Now I knew where I had seen that thick-lipped, heavy face before. I was awestruck knowing that his was the name on Bill's military dog tag.

Someone pushed a large glass of whiskey in my hand. I tried to leave it on a nearby table, the other guests were all ahead of Bill and me. I was introduced to several writers, a producer and what I took to be an actor or two. Bill plowed right in to catch up, drinking one after another. They shrieked and carried on, everyone at the same time, leaving my poor head in a blur. I was very tired, and the more tired I became the less English I could fathom. They told inside jokes about each other in the movie industry. I only half understood them but I tried to laugh anyway, so that I wouldn't appear too much of an outsider.

They howled and slapped themselves on the thighs whenever I tried to answer a question. By now I was getting used to having people laugh at my accent and took it good-naturedly from these new friends. They made Bill produce one of my last letters, and insisted I read an excerpt aloud.

I couldn't imagine what was so funny when they all exploded into gales of laughter as I reached the part about selling my beautiful embroidered "shits": "After all, Bill, my shits were handmade, and no one in America had such beautiful shits as I did." Here I interrupted my letter reading to let Bill know that the money I earned from selling all my household possessions had been stolen just before I left. He grimaced and waved away my remarks as if they didn't matter, but I noticed he poured himself another extra large drink.

Yes, it must have been hilarious and I allowed myself to be the butt of their jokes. How long this would have continued I have no idea because a tall commanding woman whose crown of frizzy red hair belied the wrinkles in her cheeks pushed open the entry door and boomed in a husky contralto, "Sorry to be late."

Richard's tenor voice chimed in, "Care for a drink, Mother, or some hash?"

My hackles rose. These friends of Bill's smoked hemp just like he did. No wonder they were so high-strung and loud. Now I realized why they never stopped moving, and were continually munching on whatever came under their hands.

The latecomer replied, "No I had quite enough at the club, thank you."

Diane said, "Boys, please don't swelter, take off your jackets and anything else you want, we won't mind, will we, Manola?"

I nodded. Bill's appearance definitely improved without his horrible zoot suit jacket and he almost looked rakish, loosening his loud tie and rolling up his sleeves. I once again admired the natural broad shoulders tapering down to his slender waist now visible in the baggy trousers.

As we were filing into the dining room, I wondered, since this was not going to be my home, why had Bill brought me here? And why did he have me write him here in the first place? Was it to fool me into thinking I would be living in one of the best districts of Los Angeles? I wanted to ask him, but now was not the time.

Dinner began with canned pears in syrup with a dollop of mayonnaise on a lettuce leaf. I watched the others as they picked up their silverware and dug in. I tested it but found the mixture of sweet and fat too cloying and foreign for my taste. What followed was a traditional American meal superbly presented: an enormous crown of rare roast beef surrounded by little brown potatoes, green beans, and asparagus, but a large ear of yellow corn with small silver corn-shaped handles sticking out of each end baffled me. Glistening with melted butter it sat glaring from the edge of my dinner plate. I watched with fascination as my companions attacked their ear of corn, trying not to drop the butter on their clothes. My expression must have been one of distaste, because Diane called down from the end of the table, "What's the matter, kid, don't you like corn on the cob?"

Everyone stopped eating, fork in mid-air, corn cob in fingers, to listen to my answer, ready to break into more laughter.

"I don't know, I never ate it before."

"So, try it," someone suggested.

"No, I don't think so," I demurred.

"Go ahead darling, you never ate corn, maybe you'll like it."

"No, I don't want to," I tried as hard as I could to be polite but with these people it was difficult.

"Well, if you won't eat it, Manola, for heaven's sake, tell us why. Everyone loves corn on the cob, how come you're the exception?"

This from yet another of the guests.

Putting down my fork and staring at each and every one in turn, "If I tell you, you won't like the reason," I said finally.

"Tell us, tell us," they chorused.

I took a deep breath. "In my country we feed it to the pigs."

Sure enough, they screamed anew and, pointing to Charles Laughton, who, as any good trencherman, had been shoveling the food in as fast as he could, someone said, "That must mean you, Charles." He shrugged noncommittally and went on eating. After dinner drinks were once again served in the living room and little by little I drew apart, feeling like a child eavesdropping at a grown-ups' party.

I listened to them comparing notes about the sexual prowess of this one and that one and was horrified. To me, sex and love were a private matter, but apparently they didn't consider love a topic at all. Sex was compared to a sport, with scoring and performance discussed like volleys at a tennis match. Their frankness made me blush.

"So when I reached for her, the damned chihuahua was between her legs," roared one of them.

The bright lights tired my eyes and I was grateful when Richard turned off the big chandelier leaving only the side sconces.

Diane and Richard danced together to some records and I watched them from the safety of the deep sofa. The low lights quieted down the others somewhat. I closed my eyes to better appreciate the music and then the unmistakable scent of hemp once again drifted across my nostrils. I recognized the sweetly acrid smell from Africa. From the lowest Arab porter to the foreign legion officer, the colonial to the American serviceman, all smoked this noxious opiate, but its cloying odor disgusted me and I felt uncomfortable in the presence of those who over-indulged.

"Why do they smoke it?" I asked Bill.

"No one else but you would've noticed, honey, you've got a great nose." And he grinned his lopsided smile, a familiar glimpse of the old Bill.

"Can we go soon, I'm so tired."

"Sure, babe, we'll get going in a little while. Don't ruin Diane's party, O.K.?"

I stifled a yawn, then a sigh, and wriggled down into the soft cushions even farther.

Finally Diane must have caught my sleepy eye, or read my mind, or both.

"Hey kids, it's getting late and this new bride must want to get home to bed, and not to sleep either. If this keeps up much longer Bill won't be worth a damn to her tonight anyway. Let's have a drink for the road."

I was so grateful, I didn't even mind when I made another of my classic boners that caused the company, now winding down, to erupt into chortles once again.

"I'm so tired," I began, "all I want is to take a douche, and go to sleep as quickly as possible."

They screamed, never having heard the French word for shower.

They all trooped out into the hallway, hugging and kissing me until I felt like a rag doll. Charles stared pointedly and drunkenly at my big square leather box with the handle on the side.

"What kind of suitcase is that?" he thundered.

"That is the home for my Paris hats," I proudly answered.

"Hats, hats," he scoffed. "My dear, this is Southern California, here *we* don't wear hats!"

On this parting shot, Bill and I were swept to our wreck of a car in a haze of alcohol and marijuana. Everyone must have had a good time, and for those few hours I forgot to think about what further deception I faced.

The cool night air calmed my flushed cheeks and I pressed my face into Bill's jacket shoulder once again.

"I'll drive you through Hollywood, baby,

you'll see bright lights and lots of people."

We drove down what he called the "Strip" and I did indeed see a lot of cars disgorging people at restaurants. Bill pointed out a sign that claimed "Ciro's" and we passed others I couldn't read fast enough.

"Don't these people ever sleep?" I asked.

"It's a night life town," he answered. I wondered how much of that night life he was involved in.

He turned off a long, dimly lit, winding street, and coasted to a stop in front of a small house, certainly not as grand as the one we had just left. He led me from the car carrying my bag and hat box and unlocked the front door. Before he flicked on the lights I had an impression of messiness in the gloom coming from the street lamps.

He showed me silently through a living room, down a long hall into the bedroom that had an attached bath.

"I'm just going to put the car away," he said, "make yourself at home."

So many unanswered questions. Was this dingy place finally to be my home? I took my nightclothes out of my suitcase, found a clean towel on the rack, washed my face — the shower would have to wait — I was too tired.

Bill returned, I heard the shower, and after a few minutes, clean and smiling, he emerged, towel draped provocatively around his hips. As he approached me, the towel fell off. Then I was in his arms and the only thing in the world that now mattered was the urgency of our bodies coming together. I wasn't as tired as I'd thought.

Birds were chattering right outside the window when I awoke in the morning. They sounded strange and when I finally opened my eyes I realized these were unfamiliar local birds.

After a hasty shower and fresh clothes I decided to let Bill sleep a little longer while I explored my new home.

Opening the front door I saw two big birds exuberantly dive- bombing each other across the lawn. I had never seen such blue- colored birds and would ask Bill what they were. Inhaling the freshness of the morning raised my mood further and I no longer felt like the same stranger in a strange land. The warmth of the sun on my skin, the smell of growing things were dear and familiar and, for the first time, I looked forward to what was to come with less fear.

I toured the house, making little notes of the changes I'd make. This is where I'll put the oriental rug, and here my Arab brassware, there my little tables. My silver service will go here. I got quite excited thinking of all the pictures I'd hang when my things arrived.

I explored the refrigerator and the cupboards. So many things were unfamiliar and then I saw the white sliced bread which I knew would never have been Bill's choice.

Everything about Bill, his clothes, his hair, and this house, his car, his friends, seemed at odds with what I thought I knew about him. He claimed to be a good cook, enjoyed gourmet food, and yet this larder was distinctly bare. Either he was very, very broke, or had been telling me a big story. I set about trying to find something for breakfast.

Eggs, well, an omelet would do. I broke half a dozen into a bowl, found butter. The toaster worked, there was coffee and a pot.

The good smell of brewing coffee finally woke him up and, rubbing his eyes sleepily, he complained about the early hour.

Excitedly I chattered about my plans for decorating the house, the strange birds I had seen and heard.

Bill ate in silence, eyes on his plate. He made no comment to any of my plans but I could see something was bothering him.

"What is it Bill," I asked. "Have I said something wrong?"

He looked up at me under his eyebrows, like a small boy expecting a chastisement. His face flushed in embarrassment. "No, no, it's not you, sweetie, I'm just having trouble trying to tell you how it is, see? This house isn't ours to change. My friend went fishing and lent it to me just for last night so that I'd have a place to bring you to sleep. He'll be home late this evening so we can have dinner here, but will have to vacate afterward. But it's O.K., I have a little place we can go, that's not the problem."

"You mean there's something else?"

I could feel my backbone stiffen at the prospect of more bad news. Please don't let it be too bad.

I forced myself to smile.

"Come on, it can't be the end of the world, cheer up."

His hangdog expression told me there was indeed more to come and it wouldn't be good.

"You see, darling, things are not what I told you in Algiers. I didn't lie to you exactly, O.K.?"

My smile felt pasted on.

"The gymnasium has gone down the tubes."

"What?"

"I knew when I was still with you in Algiers that they'd screw it up and they did."

"Who?"

"My stupid partners, that's who. I told you that when I went in the service my business interests were being taken care of by friends, right?"

I nodded.

"Well, one couldn't keep the accounts receivable separate from his gambling debts, the other had lousy public relations and scared all the legitimate customers away. Together they lost me my chance. They never paid the bills including the rent on the building for months at a time. I knew this before I left you, but thought all I had to do was show up, find some more investors, see a couple of guys, explain things, and I'd be back sailing on top, in business as before, and by the time you got here, I'd be sitting pretty."

"And now?"

"Everything has changed, babe. No one wants to know the war hero anymore. Oh sure, there's a few that'll stand me a drink, even a meal, but to invest in a new gym, no way. Money is tight, Hollywood isn't the golden dream town it was before the war, and if it wasn't for Charles, and Diane, and Richard I'd be in real big trouble."

I nodded again, silently digesting what he was telling me. Half of me believed him, but part wasn't so sure and another part outright rejected his story. What kind of a businessman leaves a business in the care of "friends"? I was no businesswoman, but even I knew that.

He continued.

"The house on Alpine Drive. I didn't mean to deceive you, I could see how excited you were when we pulled in, thinking you were going to live there. Poor kid. It just happened that I had no really permanent address, and, when Diane suggested I let you write to me care of them, of course I jumped at the chance, thinking I could straighten everything out before you came. I didn't want you to worry about anything, I knew how sad you were to leave Jean-Pierre, and I just figured, well, you know, that it'd be better not to burden you with all my problems too."

"Our problems," I said automatically. "You should've told me, Bill. I wouldn't have come, I lost all the money I had, and I wouldn't have wanted to be a millstone around your neck like I'm now. I'm sorry for all that you've been through, and, of course, it doesn't change a thing. But, I'd have liked you to have felt comfortable enough to have shared this with me."

"Sweetie, it isn't as though you were some little shop girl I picked up on the street. I saw how you lived, your people, and where you came from. I thought that, if I told you, you wouldn't want to join me, and I wanted both of you so much."

"Bill, you know me better than that; I am not that crazy about the high society life; material things are important, yes, but they don't mean everything, and, as for not bringing my son, I'm sorrier about that than you'll ever know, although it's probably better this way."

Choking back the tears, I started to cry. I didn't want to add to his pain, but the pain I was feeling took over. I had lost everything, my child, my home and security for a dubious future with a man who had no job, no prospects, and no home to bring me to.

I tried to smile through my tears. "We're young and healthy, you're very strong and smart. You'll start again, we'll build a life together, it'll be better than ready-made, you'll see. Now, where are we going to sleep tonight?"

I got up, put my arms around him and gave him a squeeze. He half smiled, squeezed me back, then said, "It's a lousy downstairs room, *m'amie*, please don't be put off me because of it."

It was a lousy room all right. It had probably been added on after the house was built, but for a basement room, it wasn't damp and, at least, didn't smell. Small and cramped, it contained a sofa, a dresser and one chair, that was all. Through a door was a tiny bathroom, everything fitted very tightly together. I tried to hide my dismay.

With a sickly smile, Bill said, "Pretty grim, huh? Sorry, kid, but, as you say, better days are ahead, and it beats sleeping in the car. Now, you have to amuse yourself for a couple of hours because I have to go out and beat the bushes."

"What?" I asked. The idea of Bill beating bushes startled me.

"You know, look for work. I hate to leave you alone your first day here, but there's food upstairs in case you get hungry and when I get back we'll figure out something."

I used up some of the time to straighten out the main house, the dishes and everything. I even dusted to feel useful, but, try as I might, the sound of the strange doves mourning outside made my already bleak mood worse and I finally sank into the sofa and burst into long-held sobs.

I cried until I was exhausted, then, head buried in my arms, fell into a troubled sleep.

When my tight and painful muscles awoke me, it took a moment to realize where I was. The realization flooded back, but some little voice down deep inside took over. "Pull yourself together," it said. And resolutely I made an attempt. I also made another pot of coffee. Sipping its warmth gratefully I assessed my situation. On the one hand I had arrived safely, in one piece after all my travails. On the other hand...I understood how alien the landscape must have seemed to Bill, when he returned from the war. All his dreams had been dashed and his hopes were at a low ebb. But how about me? My dreams were in that bottle, perhaps by now at the bottom of the sea. One thing I was sure of, I wouldn't be a burden to the already overburdened man that I had married.

I knew he wouldn't want me to cry the day away, and made certain that he'd never know how deeply he hurt me.

Rummaging through the upstairs cupboards again, I found enough ingredients to make some sort of a dinner. I changed into my most seductive dress, a favorite of his, all green, white and black pattern with a low waist and pleats jutting out from the ruffled hips.

When he came home, I greeted him with kisses and smiles. Appreciatively he sniffed the good aroma. I made him a stiff drink from the half bottle of bourbon I'd found in the cupboard. After dinner we companionably washed the dishes, straightened out the kitchen, then, turning out the lights one by one, went down to our hole.

Except for brief flashes of the man I had married, this new Bill presented himself as morose, quick to anger and violence. Because his violence wasn't directed at me, I wasn't unduly concerned.

I never knew what he was doing. When he came home late at night, "I was working," he'd explain, "you know, making money." What little money we had to live on that afforded us the succession of other little rooms, each one better than the one preceding it, came from somewhere, but I didn't know where. Eventually we were able to rent our first real apartment and all my cherished objects from home began to look right at last.

I still didn't really know what Bill was doing. With Charles's help he got some short-term work as a gate guard at Paramount, but when he'd come home with black eyes and cuts on his face, and push me away in irritation, mumbling that he had "had a match", I hadn't known he was boxing. He'd bring home "friends", most of whom I detested on sight. Often, when they visited, he'd send me to my room like a naughty child. These people were definitely not like Diane and Richard.

They were a mixed lot of wishful actors, loud with raucous, mirthless laughter. They had no conversation, only trivialities using current slang. When asked, they mumbled something about doing extra work on films for MGM or Warners, but never volunteered any information about what they were really doing to earn their living. They also freely discussed the sexual peccadilloes of the great and near-great of the screen with an omniscience that made me think they were on familiar terms with them. Most were young, a lot younger than we were. Many of them, I noticed, deferred to Bill to arbitrate on matters of physical preference.

"You knew him, am I right?" one would appeal to Bill.

"He's queer too, right?" another would say.

"You knew him, didn't you, Bill?"

Bill usually affirmed the statement, and that led me to believe that he indeed knew those people, and that all his name dropping was valid. When I questioned him about his actual "work" he still evaded or answered with "don't worry about it, sweetie, you have enough to eat, don't you?" If pressed, he became enraged, so I learned very early on not to inquire too deeply into his affairs.

Except for encouraging me to play tennis, Bill had nothing for me to do. A pair of Italian brothers owned four wisteria-shaded tennis courts next door to Grauman's Chinese theater. Bill Tilden, who was coaching Pancho Gonzalez at the time, yelled at me "are you playing tennis or the violin?", when a badly burgeoning case of tennis elbow didn't let me control my arm. Pancho was just starting out; he had a racket that pinged whenever he hit the ball, which was always. He was terrific, and I never minded lending him my racket. Other people played chess and checkers under the purple arbor, mostly actors and citizens like myself with nothing to do.

I thought about contacting Gisèle, and rooting through my papers I found the address she had scribbled. It was in some close-by section of Los Angeles reachable by bus. I hoped she was still living at the same address and decided to pay her a visit. It was a lower middle-class neighborhood, similar to my own. I rang the bell. I heard footsteps and sensed myself being observed through the peephole. I smiled and waved. After a moment the door opened on the chain.

"Manola, don't tell me it's you!"

She flung the door open and embraced me tightly as if we were going down in the same sinking ship — which we very nearly did.

"I'm so glad to see you, come in, come in." She led me to a couch against the wall, and my eyes took in a tall white lily, a single stem in a transparent blue bottle on a table near the window, the light streaming through it. Except for a window box blazing with geraniums, there was very little else to the sparsely furnished room.

"So?" I demanded. "How are you, your husband and your three children?" and I laughed at my little joke.

"Only one, so far," she smiled. "He's asleep, but you'll meet him."

I leaned over to kiss her cheek and her big blue eyes filled up with tears.

"It's so nice to see you again," she said.

"What, is anything wrong?" I asked. As usual my antennae shot up, alert to another's moods.

"Oh Manola, I'm beginning to think this was such a mistake, I love Will, and I know he loves me, but he's never home. I'm so lonely I don't know what to do with myself; if it wasn't for William Jr. and my friend, the old shoemaker, I'd be lost."

"Shoemaker? What would a shoemaker have to do with your being lonely?"

"Everything. Imagine the luck of taking in my one and only pair of shoes to a little shop in the neighborhood and finding that the shoemaker is a French Algerian Jew, elderly, very kind. He's really the only friend I have, or rather, now that you've shown up, my first friend, you're my second."

"Uhuh. I was there first," I smiled. What do

you talk about while the shoemaker fixes your shoes?"

"Everything. I tell him all my troubles, he listens, sometimes he gives me good advice, sometimes he just lets me talk."

"Let's get back to Will, your husband. He travels?" I held her hand in mine. As much as I wanted to hear about her shoemaker friend, I wanted to hear more about her Will.

"The first year was all right, he was gone a lot but came home at least on a regular basis, but this past year, I've seen less and less of him, and, just when I worry that I'll run out of money, he shows up, stays a few days, then he's gone again."

"At least you've got a roof over your head and food on the table, Gisèle, you're not cleaning houses for anyone else, you're free to raise your child. I'm sorry it took so long to look you up, I've had my dark days too, but now that we've found each other, things will be different."

I didn't want to go into my problems, that wasn't the purpose of my visit.

"What's with you?" asked Gisèle.

"I'm lonely too."

We talked for hours. Because her husband had warned her against talking or making friends with any of their neighbors and she was starving for attention, any kind of attention, Gisèle had not been able to unburden herself to anyone except David, the shoemaker. I reflected that another type of personality, a Lola or a Nadia, would have the whole neighborhood on its ear by now, but they were gregarious, magnificent women, not like this shy little retiring mouse. I would have to try to include her in some activities, she could even bring her little coffee-colored boy. This pleased her, and we decided to see each other once or twice a week.

The days hung heavy on my hands. I learned about the supermarket bulletin board and stood bemused reading the ads offering baby sitting services, housecleaning done, Spanish taught. The Spanish one caught my eye because there was an hourly rate offered. Seven dollars an hour.

If Spanish, why not French? I could earn seven dollars an hour easily, take the burden off Bill, amuse myself, and meet new people. My school days were not so far behind me. I could teach French. I needed distraction, and most of all money.

I decided not to tell Bill of my plan. I didn't want to be laughed at, or worse, have him fly into a rage at the implication that he was incapable of providing for me.

Bill's unpredictable behavior was becoming worse. Day to day I never knew what to expect of him. While his passion for me had not waned, the cool and objective observer that lived inside me, unswayed by emotion and sentiment, told me that I must learn to become independent, able to live my life on my own terms.

Diane and Richard invited us to tea, to lunch, to dinner, several times and I wanted to show them my progress in becoming acclimated. Some day, I hoped, I might be in a position to return their kind hospitality.

"He was so disappointed when you wrote that you were coming without your little boy," Diane whispered, glancing over at Bill talking with Charles, who always seemed to be at their house.

I wondered why Bill was so disappointed. For my part I was glad that my child didn't have to live in the crummy conditions that his mother had to undergo. Diane encouraged me to take the step toward teaching, so I hand-wrote several little white index cards with my telephone number, offering my French services. She had warned me to screen out the nuts, not to give out too much information, including my price.

I ended up with four legitimate students. Three ladies and one man. The man was planning postgraduate work at the Sorbonne and needed me desperately. Each took two private lessons a week, which gave my financial backing a boost.

I giggled in private at the thought of how I, the rebel who hated school, was now *Madame l'Institutrice*, teaching grammar and collecting fees.

Bill's fortunes seemed on the rise also, as once again we moved, this time to a doll house in the hills. It wasn't ours, of course; the owner, another of Bill's friends commissioned Bill and me to build the shower that had never been put into the bathroom. The house, surrounded by greenery, was tucked into the side of a hill. I loved it. We were covered in cement from head to foot day after day, but we laughed and sweated together. The work brought us close. At night we never stopped to wash, jumped in our rattletrap car, ran down to Schwab's and ate a sandwich, still covered in cement, much to the amusement of his pals.

One night not long after, lying replete from love making in Bill's arms, I decided to confess that I was a wage earner.

"What, you?" he chuckled. "How could you earn anything? You don't know anything. I think you should just leave the earning to your old man. One wage earner in this family is enough."

"I need shoes Bill, and underwear, little necessities that I don't want to ask you for. Haven't you noticed the nice food we have lately?"

"O.K., I'll bite. What have you been doing? Is it illegal, immoral, or should I be concerned?"

"I'm teaching French."

"What?" He sat bolt upright in bed. "I know you speak French, honey, but what the hell makes you think you know how to teach it?"

"I went to school, I know how it's done, I have four students and they all pay."

"Oh sure, how much can you make doing that?" he asked scornfully.

"Try two hundred dollars over the past two months," I announced smugly.

He whistled. "Wow, I'll be damned." He looked down at me with frank approval. "Not too bad, kid. Keep up the good work and maybe I can retire and you can support me, O.K.?"

I took this as an endorsement and felt better knowing he was not going to make a scene. I was relieved that he didn't find my teaching trivial as he did so many of my thoughts and ideas whenever I broached them. Every time I tried to have a serious talk he'd tease and make fun of my accent and then assure me that after some time with him I'd learn much and forget even more.

He made a fuss whenever he was having a business reversal, a bad day, or as the mood struck him. His drinking increased, and, from early morning, I grew accustomed to seeing him knock back a shot or two before he even had his coffee. He also was smoking more than his usual share of marijuana.

Once I'd made a lovely beef stew which I

knew he liked a lot. I'd worked hard on it, chopping the vegetables just right, tasting and re-tasting the gravy, it was going to be terrific. I hadn't planned on Bill coming home in such a bad mood, but one look at his eyes told me how he must have spent his afternoon.

"What's for dinner?" he growled.

"I made a lovely stew, the kind you like," I replied.

"I told you I wanted steak for dinner," he turned on me like an enraged bull.

"Oh, I don't remember that," I replied coolly, "we can have steak tomorrow night, tonight we have stew."

With a loud oath, he grasped my beautiful stewpot by its handles, kicked open the door and up-ended the pot and its contents all over the bushes. He flung the pot to the ground and stormed away.

What did I do wrong? I couldn't figure it out. I was beginning to be very afraid of Bill.

His friendship or dependency on Charles Laughton was upsetting too. They smoked a lot together, and the acrid smell hung in the air for hours after Charles left. Usually they wanted to be alone and I was sent to my room. I never complained.

"Here, try it," Charles insisted on one of the rare occasions I was allowed to stay, mainly because they had come laden with all sorts of delicious pastries.

"No, I don't want to try it," I replied.

"Oh come on, get with it, just take a puff, hold it in your lungs and see what happens. How can you judge something you never tried, like the corn on the cob."

That stung. Defiantly I took the proffered joint and inhaled deeply. Then, with a glance at Bill who was watching open-mouthed, I did it again. And again.

Suddenly I heard a loud cry. Evidently it came from me.

"I'm falling, help me, I'm falling!"

I was standing on the narrowest of mountain peaks. Narrow, because there was room for one of my feet, but not for the other. I tried to find a place for my other foot, but I was toppling. Bill caught me in his strong arms and, clasping me to him, said, "That's it for you, baby. You don't touch the stuff again." He laid me on the couch and I heard them talking together as if they were very far away. My mind wouldn't stop whirling, and my eyes were so heavy I just wanted to sleep. After a while Bill picked me up and took me to bed.

As time went on, Bill's personality quirks that I had thought peculiar, became frightening. There were many nights of interrupted sleep when I'd be jolted awake by Bill lashing out at the air, screaming and fighting an imaginary adversary. "What's wrong, what is it?" I'd demand.

"Nothing to do with you, I'll kill him, I'll kill him," he'd shout, shaking with rage.

"Who, who is it?" I'd ask again, trying to calm him.

"Don't you hear it, they're all outside, they want to get in, but I won't let them, I'll protect you."

He was reliving something, somewhere between a nightmare and an hallucination. When I asked about it in the morning, he'd give me a funny look and deny it, or pass it off as a bad dream. Those were the most realistic bad dreams I ever witnessed from anyone.

Throughout he managed to earn a living with what I thought were his pick-up jobs. I had learned never to ask, never to probe; through a series of events, however, I found out he was a bookmaker. Everyone loved to play the horses, but they didn't go to the track to do it. It seemed that half of Hollywood played the horses with my husband. One night one of his clients phoned. She was the madam of a local brothel, had won big on the races, but Bill was holding out on her. He must have been leveraging his money elsewhere and, knowing her reputation, thought he could stall her.

"I'll pay you when I can, don't threaten me, toots," his voice was menacing. "If you make a stink about this, you'll find it hard to walk on two broken legs."

Franchot Tone, the actor, wanted his money too, and I was dashed to realize that one of my favorite movie stars was as wicked as this stranger I had married.

Bill's business office was at the Ben Ruben Market, next door to Schwab's. I found it amazing that even though many people, mainly men, were always milling around in front and inside, I never actually saw anyone purchase a large amount of groceries. It took me quite a while to figure out that the store was a mere front for a bookmaking establishment.

He gambled at other things too. One night he was showering for the third time, getting ready to go out, carefully choosing a somber tie, brushing his best dark suit.

"It's Easter Sunday, Bill, can't you spend a little time with me?" I begged. I hated to ask him, but I didn't want to be left alone again.

He looked at me sideways through the mirror, under his blond brows. "You really want to come?"

"Oh yes, please!" I was excited, he hardly ever took me anywhere and to go with him on a business meeting was heady stuff.

"Wear that blue dress I like, you look good in that, and put your hair up on top, it's more sophisticated."

"Where are we going?" I asked, hurrying through my preparations as he was already drumming his fingers in impatience.

High up in the hills we finally reached a big mansion, surrounded by trees and cut off from prying eyes that might venture off the road.

I thought it was a party, there were so many cars. A gangster type opened the door and we climbed the richly carpeted stairs to an upper floor.

There were people in evening clothes, the smoke hung heavy in the air from their cigars and cigarettes. I followed at Bill's heels like his puppy, fearing to let him out of my sight.

Everywhere were instruments of gambling. Billiard tables, baccarat, roulette wheels, card games, the noise was deafening, they were all trying to talk at once.

Bill slapped a few shoulders, was greeted in turn. He seemed to know everyone, and everyone knew him. He only introduced me to two couples.

I wasn't familiar with pool, but I thought I knew something wrong when I saw it.

Standing casually at the end of the table, Bill watched the play for a moment, then palmed one of the balls right off the table with the intention of pocketing it, therefore causing the player to lose.

Without thinking, my moral outrage took center stage. "What are you doing, you took a ball," I shouted loud enough for the whole room to hear.

He glared at me, then, realizing all eyes were upon us, smiled charmingly and, with a shrug, replaced the ball on the table.

One of the men from the group of players neared, took Bill aside and had some heated words. It ended with Bill laughing, and, still laughing, he took my arm. "Come on, we're going, this was not the place to bring you, I should have known better."

"Is this is your business, Bill, cheating people? Is that what you do for a living?" The blindfold dropped and I was certain that, although I still admired the raw animal courage and daring he possessed, I didn't really like him as a person anymore.

I was furious, but he steered me down the stairs and out into the night as fast as possible.

On our way home, he pulled into the curb at Sunset and Laurel Canyon. Ruthie, the old newspaper vendor, came over to tell Bill about someone who owed her a large sum of money, and wasn't making any effort to repay it.

"He's a lawyer now, just a young punk — you know him. I helped him out, you know, like I used to do with you, Bill." He probably shot her a warning glance because she didn't pursue that direction of her story.

"He promised to give me the money back within two weeks, but here it's been a month, and he's ducking me, Bill, what can I do?"

"Sweetheart, leave it to me, O.K.?" Bill could swagger, even sitting down.

Suddenly, like a guard dog, Bill sat up straight. He turned off the engine, opened the door and raced across Sunset Blvd., dodging traffic. Horns blared, motorists shouted at him to get out of the street. I saw his quarry look up in alarm. Bill had seized the collar of a young man's jacket and was holding him up so that his feet couldn't touch the ground. My heart was beating so fast, I thought it would fall into the hole in my stomach. People were watching on both sides of the street and traffic slowed to a crawl.

I couldn't see what else happened until the man pulled out a wallet, extracted some bills and gave them to Bill. He sauntered back across the wide boulevard waving and smiling to his acquaintances. He reached the car safely and handed Ruthie the money. She was so grateful, but he cut short her effusive thanks, jumped back in the car and we roared away.

"That son of a bitch, not for anything was he going to get away with cheating her."

Really, this man was a contradiction. So cruel to me, but so protective of a newspaper vendor.

More than ever, I knew that I would have to take steps to meet people on my own, to go out into the world without Bill. I realized once again that we were two people who could never be happy together.

Proof of it came when the one and only young American couple I had met, came to supper, stayed late and couldn't get home because the husband was too drunk to drive.

"*M'amie*, do you love me?" Bill asked out of the blue later that night in our bedroom.

"What? Why do you ask?"

"I never asked you for anything, have I?"

"No-o-o, but what is it?"

"Now be honest, isn't it true, that I have never asked you for anything, right?"

"Yes, yes, it's true, what are you driving at?"

"*Chérie*, be a pal, go downstairs and get Anne, and bring her here, O.K.?"

I sprang up, out of bed, thinking it was a joke.

"Sure Bill, I'll do it, be right back."

I started down the steps, then sat down, head in hands and waited for a few minutes. No, it wasn't a joke.

Now back in our bedroom, I exploded, "You son of a bitch, how can you ask me such a thing? I'm your wife and Anne is married to Gilbert, what kind of a person are you anyway?"

He tried to take me in his arms and kiss me, but I was not to be mollified. Not this time. I pushed him away, curled up in a ball on my side of the bed and tried to put the ugliness out of my mind.

CHAPTER 9

I WANTED TO MEET other people like myself — if we were seven war brides on one troop ship, why then, there must have been many more on many more ships. Perhaps I could find the North African ones and meet them. Perhaps I could even form a little club or something like that. I was so lonely that the idea took over and became the pivot point of my thoughts.

Drawing upon my experience with Lola and the consul in Baltimore I marched into the French consulate and requested to see the man in charge. Without any trouble I was shown to his office and found him to be charming and outgoing.

"I'm a war bride, and bored to tears, not working, how much tennis can one play?" I asked.

He spread his hands, noncommittal, unsure of what I wanted.

"Maybe you can help me. I'd like a list of other war brides from my country, North Africa, their phone numbers, so that I could start a little club because I'm sure some are as lonely as I, and would welcome the sound of our own French in each other's ears."

He laughed out loud, and provided me with the list I needed. I went right to work.

"Hello, I'm a war bride like you from Algiers and I thought it might be nice if we could start a little club where we could all meet and talk. I got your

171

name and number from the French consul."

Their responses ranged from mild interest to great enthusiasm. My original idea, girls only, was swamped by Bill, who insisted that we also include the husbands.

"Not in any way am I having my home filled with a bunch of females without some male company too," he said.

I thought to include Gisèle, whether her husband Will was in town or not. It would be fun for her to meet others like herself, and exchange stories. Perhaps she'd see that she was not as alone as she thought. The day I phoned her was completely by chance, but her news was so eventful I completely forgot the purpose of my call.

"Manola, you won't believe this," her voice was somber and I imagined her standing, looking out the cheerless window, perhaps dead-heading the geraniums as she propped the phone next to her ear. "You haven't heard from me lately because Will has been home, and it was so wonderful having him here, just like a honeymoon. We took the baby and went to some nice restaurants and he bought me some new clothes."

"And then?" I knew there was going to be a punch line to this story I might not want to hear.

"And then. Well. He left, and just this morning I was going to send the suit that he left here to the cleaner, and what do you think I found in the pocket?"

"I don't know, tell me."

"A cleaning receipt, from a dry cleaner in Oakland, that's up by San Francisco."

"So?"

"So, Manola, this one had three women's

dresses on it, a woman's blouse and a man's suit."

"Oh, I see."

"No, I don't think you do. I called the phone number listed under Will's name, and, when a woman answered, I asked to speak to Will and she asked...," and here Gisèle's voice faded away.

"What did she ask?" I pressed on, determined to hear the end of the story.

"She wanted to know what I needed with her husband," and now Gisèle was sobbing in earnest. I stood stock-still, my feet turned to icy blocks.

"Oh, Manola, what could I do? I heard children's voices, big children, in the background. This is why he's always away. He had another family before he married me, doesn't that make him a bigamist?"

"Yes, it does, but what are you going to do about it?"

"What can I do? I have no money, a child, and no prospects, I want to be gone from here, I'd even go back to Algeria to work as a maid, anything but this existence."

"Well, without any money, you can't really go anywhere, why don't you get out of the house, do you want to come over?" I had remembered the original purpose of my call, but decided not to invite her to the party in her present state. I tried to put her out of my mind for now, and concentrate on my gathering, but I had a hard time and couldn't stop thinking about her, her aureole of pale blond hair and blue eyes like a Botticelli angel.

Our house had a large terrace, a grotto with a fish pond, and Bill installed lights in the trees and equipment so that the music could be piped outside for dancing on the patio.

I outdid myself with a big minted lamb soup, a charba, and a large paella, loaded with shrimp, chicken and pork which looked and smelled divine. Bill bought beer and soft drinks and seemed as excited as I was. Of course any excuse to meet a new skirt was a welcome occasion, but I tried not to think about that.

The eleven girls, with their husbands, were to bring only little desserts if they chose, but nothing else this first time. Their turn to entertain would come later.

At first we all got on famously. The men were about the same age, except for Bill, who was the oldest. They got together in a group away from us girls, drank, and re-fought the battles of the war. All the girls were younger than me, and from all over North Africa. Some from Oran, some from Algiers, some from Casablanca. Some had children and showed their pictures; we talked into the night, we danced, we ate, we laughed and cried. But as the liquor took effect, they flirted, some shamelessly, with each other's husbands.

I hadn't counted on that.

We must have met perhaps four or five more times within as many months. Each time at a different house, and, by the fifth party, I was sure they were pairing off.

Although Bill was the oldest, his eye was caught by Yvette, the youngest war bride. She'd been only fifteen when she married her G.I. and in many ways was still a child. When it was their turn to entertain in Burbank, she showed such great pride in her new vacuum cleaner, dragging us to the closet to show it off, just like a little girl with her latest toy.

Their party was the last. I caught Bill dancing cheek to cheek with her while her drunken husband dozed off. Bill was kissing her neck and, when I confronted him, said he'd had too much to drink.

"You should be ashamed, she's so young and you're old enough to be her father," I raged. "I don't want to continue with this anymore. Sophie, the one from Oran, has already broken up two marriages, her own, as well as Suzanne's, by taking her husband away. What kind of people are they? This wasn't what I had in mind when I started and I'm so disgusted, I wish I'd never begun this project. I'm sorry for the day I thought of doing it."

Bill, as usual, just shrugged and the war bride club was over before it really had a chance to begin.

I was lonelier than ever. I didn't care for the people I met through Bill, with the exception of a very few effete young men. Charles pulled back from his friendship or guardianship of Bill, and rarely visited anymore. I didn't miss him, but I felt Bill did.

One day Ramon Navarro came to lunch. "Hey, there's a new arrival in town," he announced. "She's a yoga teacher up on the top of Franklin."

My ears perked up. I had studied yoga when I visited India with my father.

"Is she Indian?" I asked.

"No, she's Lithuanian, I think. She lives very simply in one room where she sleeps, cooks and teaches. You should go with me, she's fascinating."

I looked to Bill for approval and, without raising his eyes, he nodded.

Gita did indeed live in one room, high on a hill overlooking Hollywood. The gold trimmed Chinese-looking building glittered under the sun; I felt immediately at home there.

So began, from a chance conversation over lunch, my career as a yoga teacher. But all that followed in good time.

Bill had returned from yet another of his unexplained absences. I hated to be alone and welcomed him warmly. I had just come home from teaching and wanted to take a shower; he followed me in, as he did frequently. Once it had been exciting but now it made me nervous. I never knew what to expect.

"Turn around," he ordered.

I did so.

"Cute," he said.

"What?" I asked.

"Your ass. It's like a little boy's ass, so cute," he repeated.

My stomach twisted. A little boy's ass indeed. How lucky I was not to have brought my son with me. Who knows what kind of a father Bill would have been? With his drinking, drugs, bad habits, gambling, the associations he kept, who knows what depredation he might have visited upon my innocent child? Perhaps my ex-husband had done us a favor after all. I realized that Bill was a colossal liar and we became more and more alienated.

He seemed ambivalent about me. I often had the feeling he was trying to throw me into the arms of another man. Why? Was it to prove to himself that I was as unfaithful as he thought all women were? Or was it to be rid of me? He had little patience and would pick a fight over almost nothing at all.

On one occasion, when I was teaching one of my French lessons to a handsome young man at home, I looked up to see a glaring mask staring through the window. I was startled but continued on as if I hadn't noticed anything. I glanced again, the eyes that confronted mine were pools of angry hate. A few moments later Bill came in acting in his normal way, his face flushed, and again I had a sinking feeling in my stomach. He seemed determined to catch me doing something wrong.

His mercurial mood swings led to violent temper tantrums. A next door neighbor who had the unfortunate habit of blocking our driveway with his car got the full brunt of Bill's displeasure. After warning the man several times in his usual unpleasant manner, Bill saw his chance to make a lasting impression. Running down the stairs as the neighbor was revving up his car to leave, Bill exploded, "I warned you, didn't I? Not once or twice, but many times. Don't park in front of my driveway."

Bill reached in, grabbed the man's coat collar from the back, and hauled him out the open window. Fueled by his choleric anger, his phenomenal strength made me fearful that he'd really harm the poor unfortunate. Needless to say, the neighbor never parked in front of our driveway again.

I was so alone. I had neglected Gisèle because I couldn't take the burden of her problem on my plate, having enough of my own. But that wasn't what friendship was all about. I finally called, half-expecting the telephone to be disconnected and was surprised when she answered on the first ring, her hello gay and upbeat.

I thought I had the wrong number. "Gisèle, is that you?"

"Manola, I was just going to call you to say good-bye."

"What do you mean, good-bye? Where are

you going?" I asked.

"Wonderful news, really, be happy for me. David, my shoemaker friend offered to take care of Jr. and me, and we're leaving for home in a few days."

"Home? What do you mean?"

"Algeria. He wants to retire, and he'll take me as his daughter-housekeeper-whatever and he's promised to raise the boy as his own grandchild. You know, he's as alone in the world as I am, has a little money put by, and really, Manola, we're so comfortable together, I think we'll be happy. No one knows I'm going and I want to be out of this place before Will has a chance to come back looking for me."

Of the seven of us, Lola, Arlette and Gisèle either had their fates sealed or sealed their own. What would happen to me? To Nadia? Of Emma and Marie I had no doubt they, in their modest expectations, their very practicality, would be able to muddle along somehow; they were survivors, perhaps more so than the rest of us.

I took to walking in the hills for hours, it was my favorite way to quiet my mind and feed my spirit. I usually followed the same road and my little journey wound past a house where a woman tended her garden. She'd wave in a neighborly fashion, I'd shyly wave back. After a few days of these across-the-road exchanges, she called me over. "Come on, you look hot, come and have a drink."

The woman was blond, elegant, smartly dressed in tailored pants. Even doing her gardening, she looked cool and collected.

"How about a Seven-Up?" she asked.

"What's that? I don't drink alcohol," I warned.

"No, nothing of the kind, it's something that makes you burp," she laughed.

"I drink Coca-Cola for that," I said. "This will be my first Seven-Up."

She had a lovely home, as elegant as she was. There was a grand piano in the living room and I envied her the magnificent instrument, I hadn't played since I'd left home.

She smiled at me.

"So tell me, who are you?"

"I'm Manola Thompson."

Her eyes opened wide and she gasped.

"Not Bill Thompson's new French wife?"

"Yes, that's me," I admitted.

"Oh my poor dear girl," she clucked, commiserating.

Why, what did she mean?

"Are you aware that you are wife number five?" she asked.

I stared at her. Carefully I replaced my glass on the little table before trusting myself to answer.

"No, I wasn't aware of that."

"Bill has a habit of marrying 'em and leaving 'em," she said. "I've known three out of four, and they were all great gals, although each one had her little faults."

"Faults, what kind of faults?" I was numb.

"Oh, one turned out to be a classical lush, he found her keeping company with the whiskey bottle once too often, and one combed her hair over the sink and he hated that, and another one ...."

I cut her off. "Are you absolutely sure about this," I asked, "how do you know my Bill?"

"Honey, everyone knows your Bill, and I've had him and his various wives here many times. He's a character, but are you telling me you really didn't know about the others?"

"No," I admitted. "He never told me, and I never asked. He was so charming when I met him in Africa. His energy, his humor, his gifts for making me laugh, I loved that about him. How was I to know I wasn't the first wife he ever married?"

"Well, I'm sorry to be the one to burst your bubble, kid, and I hope it doesn't get me in trouble with your old man, my telling you, that is. After all, it really only matters who's in the driver's seat now, and that's you, right?"

I nodded.

I didn't hear much of the rest of what she told me about herself, her house, her son or anything else. My mind was like a tongue probing a sore tooth, I couldn't let it go, and I couldn't stop. How was I going to handle this? I knew it would blast out of me like an exploding volcano and I was almost afraid for the consequences.

After many promises to come back and play duets with her on the gorgeous grand piano, I left and strode purposefully home. I wasn't sure what I was going to do, but, unlike anything else, I couldn't let this one drift by.

He was home ahead of me. Pacing and looking stormy about the brows. What had happened?

I saw the mail on the table. He had a post office box in the local station and usually brought the mail home with him at night. I never got to see it unless there were letters for me.

This evening there were letters for me. Bill was ominously silent as I put the final touches on our dinner. I tried to lighten the mood by chattering about the nice lady and my first Seven-Up. I wondered about the mail.

I knew there was one from Arlette. From across the room I recognized her spidery scrawl on the envelope, but the one that scared me a little had a Newport Beach post mark and what looked like a return address from Al White.

My heart skipped several beats in reconstructing the letter I'd written him when I was at my lowest ebb, not long after my arrival. I forgot what I told him, but instinctively knew that he might comment on it and was apprehensive.

"Aren't you going to open your mail?"

"Oh, after dinner, no hurry." I tried to be as casual as possible. No point arousing him further by my excitement or interest in what the letters might contain.

"Who's this one from?" He waved the Newport envelope.

"Oh, Al White, how nice, the first mate on the boat, you know, I told you all about how kind he was to us."

"I thought so," Bill replied gruffly. "How the hell did he get this address? And why should he write you unless you wrote him letting him know you were here?"

"Oh Bill, don't be silly, he only wanted to be sure I got to the West Coast and to you safely. I wrote a note to tell him that. I didn't expect a return letter."

"Sure, it's normal for a guy who spends months on a ship with a girl to write to her after she gets to her husband," and he glowered even more.

"Go on, open it." He flung the letter at me.

I allowed myself a moment's pause, I recognized the address as his sister's and the image of the boyish yet masculine first mate swam into view in my mind's eye.

The letter, a note really, only expressed Al's concern for my welfare and repeated once again his offer of assistance should I need it. It ended with a few little innocent French phrases I'd taught him in the wheelhouse those long nights when we were revealing ourselves to each other, phrases I'd never have taught him had I foreseen the results.

Bill snatched the letter from me when a little smile inadvertently played around my lips. I stood by while he read it, his neck and face flushed a deeper red, the veins on his forehead began to pulse. This was going to be one of his more spectacular rages and, in spite of myself, I trembled.

He tore the letter into tiny pieces, venting his anger on the paper, ripping and mutilating it.

He turned on me, grabbed me by the hair, pulled me close and, shoving his face into mine, shouted, "My wife, my French wife is nothing but a French whore. Only thirty lousy days to wait, but no, she had to get some, so she screws some swabby on her ship."

I tried to remonstrate, but he wouldn't let me.

"Don't try to deny it, baby, this guy was screwing you and you liked it. No man who wasn't doing it would call another man's wife, his petite femme, what a nerve he has to write you in such an intimate way. He wants you to see his sister, fine, toots, you're going to see her. Get packed, you're leaving, I've had enough."

His accusations hammered at me like physical blows and I tried to shrink away, making myself as small as I could. He grabbed my wrist and dragged me to the closet where we kept our luggage. He reached for my suitcase and threw it on the floor.

"Here, pick it up, pack your rags and get out."

He pushed me away viciously, I screamed and hurled myself at him, trying to get him to listen to me, but he was implacable.

He trapped my hands between his and brutally forced me to my knees; what did he want, only to show his superior strength and his contempt? He punched me and I fell over sideways, unable to resist the attack.

I lay on my side, fetus-like, gulping air as I sobbed. He watched in stony silence. I sat up. He was carefully folding my clothes, very precisely packing my toilet articles. His meticulous calm added to my horror.

This can't be happening, a voice screamed inside my head. But yes, it was happening.

I was overwhelmed by panic, but took several deep breaths and finally found my voice.

"Bill, how can you treat me like this, I'm your wife."

He was no longer flushed and coolly appraised me with eyes like shards of ice, the cold blue eyes of a stranger.

"He was just being kind to me, don't you see, there was never anything between us, how can you jump to conclusions like that? You dishonor me, you make me ashamed that you could even think such a thing. As God is my judge, he was never more than a friend, Bill, please, you must believe me."

"Don't give me that shit, baby," he said. "I know women, and I know you like a book, so don't try to kid me. You're one of the hottest babes I've ever known, and, believe me, I've known plenty."

I knew it would be like throwing gasoline on

a roaring fire to confront him with his infidelities as far as our marriage vows were concerned, so I swallowed and said nothing, not even about what I had learned that afternoon.

"You're never going to make me believe that a hot babe could go without it for so long with a good-looking stud around to do the job. No woman would, I've never trusted any of them, any one of them would do the same if given half the chance. Don't think I wasn't getting my share waiting for you to arrive, so why wouldn't you do the same? Sure, I tried to kid myself that you'd be different, but all the time, down deep, I knew you were a whore just like all women are, naturally. That letter showed me all the proof I needed, too bad I tore it up, it would be grounds for divorce from any judge in the world. No man who hadn't been there lots of times would write such things, you'll never make me believe otherwise."

I tried to tell him that I loved only him, and I could only give myself when I loved truly and deeply, but he wouldn't listen, didn't want to hear what I had to say in my own defense.

I finally gave up. I only heard a portion of Bill's ranting. I paid attention when he shook me and shouted in my face.

"Come on, get your ass out of that chair, get moving, you're leaving. I don't care where you go, even to your boy friend's sister, it's all the same to me, you're not staying here one more minute."

I followed him blindly out of the house to the car. He tossed my battered suitcase into the back and jumped in the driver's seat, leaving me to open my own door. Before I could close it, in his mad hurry, he'd already pulled away from the curb. I withdrew further into my shell, to the farthest corner, away from him. We drove for some time, me not comprehending our direction nor much caring about the destination. I was hardly aware when he ground to a stop, got out and pulled out my bag.

"Well, come on, what are you waiting for? This is the end of the line for you, toots."

I found myself on the sidewalk fronting the long park-like boulevard between two major streets in Beverly Hills. I recognized the City Hall. There were benches, I had seen it before, marveled at how pretty this was in the middle of the city, a park too small for large congregations of people, but just right for lovers, or a stroll with a friend. I looked up at Bill.

"Look, baby, this is it. This is good-bye. You drag your bag and your ass over to one of those benches, and I drive away and that's it. Whatever you do, and wherever you go, is up to you. You're a good-looking broad and some guys come through here on their way someplace else," and he swept his arm toward the expanse of the green park. "With any luck you'll get picked up fast and, if you play your cards right, you'll make enough to get fixed up in a new place by morning."

He turned on this parting shot and I watched his red tail lights disappear down the street. I automatically did as he said. Picked up the bag and marched to the nearest bench. Was this really happening? I huddled on the bench, my mind in a whirl, trying to sort out, to make some kind of sense of this. It was impossible. This Bill was not the man I had known, he was a monster and the world had become an alien, unforgiving place. For comfort, I retreated to hug my own inner flame.

Catatonia set in and although I was vaguely aware of the very few men, and women too, who walked by, stared at me curiously and continued on, none of them stopped to speak. My abject lack of response to their presence was so strong that no one dared to offer assistance even if they cared to.

The evening wore on into night which grew colder, but I hardly noticed it. The physical discomfort didn't register; it simply became part of the outer world which I had voluntarily rejected. I felt as if I was bleeding to death. All my energy turned to guarding the life flame deep inside which sputtered and flickered like a candle nearing its end. Slowly, so slowly, the sky lightened, birds began to awake and scold, and occasional cars began to pass, the whisper of their tires loud in the emergence of the dawn.

On I sat, oblivious, until a hand on my shoulder aroused me.

I raised my head.

"Come on, get up, I'll take you home."

I followed Bill to the car, resumed my self-protective position in the corner as far from him as I could.

"Shut the door," he commanded.

I didn't move. He was still angry and swore when I didn't respond. He had to lean across me to pull the door shut, and as I smelled his peculiar odor of alcohol and aftershave my stomach turned.

I reached the bedroom and, without a pause, stepped out of my shoes, climbed into bed, and pulled the covers up over my head, effectively shutting out Bill and the rest of the world.

Curled in my tight ball, I awoke many hours later. I was vaguely conscious of smelling my own odor in the clothes I still had on. I listened. Nothing.

I was alone in the house. Cautiously I stretched, the late afternoon sun picked up the fine hairs on my forearms which I studied with great absorption. I had never noticed how fine a work of art they were. I could move them with my breath and this fascinated me. Slowly other things registered, I heard the loud ticking of the bedside clock, the neighbor's lawn-mower, felt the rough texture of the blanket I was still half wrapped in. I was aware of the delicious aroma of fresh-cut grass, other things flooded in, then suddenly, with the clamor of a window being thrown open on a busy street, I was inundated with stimuli of all kinds, mind racing, eager to be back in the world again.

I was alone. Bill must have slept on the sofa. I noticed the half-empty whiskey bottle, a glass, an overflowing ash tray.

It was the end. Or the beginning of the end. From that day onward, we skirted each other like a pair of nervous dogs. The few times he returned home we barely spoke. For my part, I was too afraid of provoking another incident. He growled at me when he wanted something, and in general treated me like hired help. I led a monotonous life, alone and deprived of love or even human attention.

To live with the knowledge that the man I had loved, not only didn't love me, but actually abhorred me, magnified my desire to go home. I couldn't feel that I had changed, but I found myself looking closely in the mirror to find a trace of whatever it was that made me so loathsome to Bill. He was unmistakably a dangerous lunatic. No sane man would treat his wife as he had treated me. What other warped and twisted ideas were incubating beneath that surface?

I continued to teach French and yoga, and saved every penny. I just hated to leave the little house that I loved so much.

Gita's yoga school was my salvation. After the classes, I'd sit on the steps and let the breeze caress my cheeks like the lips of a tender lover. The view was golden, the light luminous. Sighing, the breeze and I dreamed in those moments of long delight, my spirit lifted, was free, and the overwhelming pain that coursed through my being disappeared. All too soon I'd have to regain reality in my empty house where bleakness was my only future and sadness a devouring mouth.

I was like a fish on a line, hooked, yet too tired to fight any longer, aware of being reeled inexorably toward an uncertain fate. One day the line snapped.

While cleaning an unused chest I found a carefully hidden packet of letters in the back of one of the drawers. They were obscured by old utility bills and I could easily have overlooked them. I recognized some of my own letters, and leafed past those, but my eye was caught by another feminine hand on some other envelopes, so I opened them. A pretty face stared out at me, short curly hair, round cheeks and bright laughing eyes. I stared back at her photo before reading her letter. Her breezy, witty style, full of passion and hope, tried to recreate the life they had together. The letters were dated from 1945 through 1946. I gasped. Bill and I were just getting married then. Who was this girl? And why had I never known about her? I read on avidly, she had quite a long history with Bill, even accompanying him to camp when he shipped out for Italy. They'd had a house, a car together, and yet, between the lines, I could sense her unhappiness. Finally I reached the most recent letters which caused me to feel her despair as if she was in the same room with me. She had been expecting Bill's child. I stopped reading and realized that he had abandoned her at this crucial stage of her life, and for what? For me. I felt ashamed, knowing that, because the war had set its trap for us, I was the instrument by which Bill wounded her so badly. Here was my Beau Brummell breaking yet another heart, how many had he broken that I had no knowledge of? There were some obvious parallels between this Arlene and myself. Had I been able to look into a crystal ball back then, I could have avoided the anguish for both of us. Her last letter, dated late in 1946, announced the death of her little boy, who never lived to see his first birthday.

Tenderly I re-closed the letters in their envelopes, and caressed the packet with my open palm. He had no right to ruin her life as well as mine. He had no right to keep our letters either, and I took both packets.

No, he had no right.

My resolve formed. My decision made, without another thought, I began to pack my clothes. The words of a French song popular during the war echoed in my ears and I began to sing aloud. No man is worth the pain. He had inflicted more distress on me than anyone should ever be allowed to. I knew I could face whatever life threw at me now. I hummed as I moved swiftly about the house, taking with me only what I required for my immediate needs. I felt alive, felt the well-being that came from a well-made decision, one that I could live with, alone, on my terms. I knew I could make my own way for myself, I wasn't afraid of hard work. I was confident. It was over.

CHAPTER 10

WITH THE HELP of a friend, I rented a room in the apartment of an old lady who needed help. I continued to teach yoga at Gita's studio, French at other people's houses, and scrambled to make ends meet. I didn't have much in reserve but at least I was eating regularly thanks to my other pick-up jobs in two restaurants.

Receiving mail was a problem, I couldn't lose the connection with my son, and perhaps I might not be with Gita forever. I decided to invest some of my slender resources in a P.O. Box so that, if I moved, I could always be reached.

Shortly after I had written Arlette in New York to tell her that I had left Bill, a bulky letter with a colorful foreign stamp arrived from her.

"Dearest Manola," she began. "I wished that you had a telephone because what I'm going to tell you will take a while and it's not pleasant. Charles, up until now, had stood firm on not letting me look for an apartment on Park Avenue and we were still living in his dark, cramped bachelor digs in Brooklyn, which I just hated, but he kept fobbing me off with excuses one after the other and now it's academic as I've discovered that the man I married is a liar."

I pursed my lips and shook my head. What was coming next?

"On Monday, having nothing to do as usual,

and being bored to death, I decided to take a taxi into Manhattan and do a little shopping."

I reflected on how different her life with generous Charles was from mine with its constant penny-pinching. I knew that he gave her a more than liberal allowance which he encouraged her to spend on herself. She had often bragged how he was continually shoving money in her purse urging her to "buy yourself something pretty."

Poor Arlette, anyone else in her position would volunteer at a hospital, work with under-privileged children, go back to school and learn English properly — but Arlette was selfish and self-centered and, even though I had suggested those avenues in many of my letters, she chose to be bored to death rather than be of help to anyone else, or even to get her well-manicured hands dirty.

"That Monday I decided to go to Macy's, Charles's family store where I've been shopping many times. For some reason I had the urge to start on the eighth floor and take the escalator down, examining each floor in turn. Perhaps I could help make some suggestions that would enhance the store's operation. I'd never been on the eighth floor because I knew it was all food and I never had the need to shop for groceries — Charles always took care of that, bringing home lovely prepared meals as well as all the necessaries. We ate out a lot too, so there was no reason for me to explore that eighth floor. I was just astounded to see the wonderful variety of shops, foodstuffs, and all sorts of good things. There was a pastry shop, a bakery, a delicatessen, a fish market, a meat market, stalls filled with pyramids of fresh fruit and vegetables, gourmet items, candy, canned and packaged goods from around

the world, as well as a coffee bar full of people. I just
stood with my mouth open, so surprised and a little
put out that Charles never told me about this mar-
velous bazaar. The crowds of shoppers, mostly
women, eddied about and jostled one another and
me, but at one point I was alone in the middle of the
floor and that's when it happened. Manola, you
won't believe what I saw. A pack of women clustered
around one of the shop stalls, laughing and joking
with a big burly butcher, complete with blood-
stained apron and little flat white headgear. It was
my Charles."

I inhaled sharply and read on.

"He was cutting chops, ringing up purchases,
making change and waving good-bye to departing
customers with a huge toothy grin I'd never seen
before. Eyes flashing with good humor and personality, he was like a professional actor and I was so
shocked that my feet were rooted to the ground and
unable to carry me away. He spotted me in that
same instant; his face blanched, fell, all smiles gone,
and I could hear him gasp. He reached out to me
and on his white face I read the embarrassment, the
chagrin, the knowledge that now he knew I knew
about him. There was no pretense any longer. He
called in a strangled voice, 'Arlette, darling, wait,' but
I was already halfway to the elevator, he was puffing
behind me. 'I meant to tell you, honestly I did, but I
could see it wouldn't have pleased you to know that
my family had owned only this concession for many
years and it was what put my brothers and me
through college. I know you think you married the
colonel whose family had the entire store, and I just
couldn't bring myself to tell you until I was sure you
loved me as much as I love you. I'm so sorry, will you

ever forgive me?' The elevator doors opened. Perhaps you, Manola, will think it bad of me, but I truly couldn't help myself as I flung over my shoulder that no butcher's bloody paws were ever going to touch me again. The door closed on his stricken face and, to say that I was mortified in that elevator full of his customers, is putting it mildly. I shrank down into my coat collar and bolted for the street as soon as the elevator doors opened.

Not much more to report. I booked a flight home, called my father, yanked open my closets and dresser drawers, dragged everything out, pitched the last nightie he gave me on the floor, hurled stuff into my bags, didn't even leave a note — he'd figure it out — and here I am, dear Manola. You probably think I was hasty and even a little cruel, but, you know, I wasn't ever raised to be a butcher's wife, I had expected better for myself, and of course my family's happy to have me home. It was all a big mistake. Please write as soon as you can, all my love."

Charles's war-time work uniform had attracted the bee to the flower, but his civilian work clothes also hastened his end. I felt sorry for him, more than for her, and imagined the solitary little bouquet of flowers he may have bought on his way home that final rainy night, abandoned on the table, deprived of attention, its sweet message never reported, slowly shriveling to a dry vestige of its former beauty.

Through letters, and phone calls spanning some good measure of time, I learned that Nadia had gone to school, that her husband's family had struck oil on their property making Rich an instant millionaire, providing the type of life all of us on board that fateful ship would have wanted for ourselves.

During her marathon telephone calls she exuberantly related he new life. "Rich took me to Neiman-Marcus, the very best department store, immediately headed for the *designer* dresses, and started to dictate to the saleslady what he wanted me to wear. Do you know he even pointed out that I wasn't the typical Texas type, but rather short-waisted and he wanted to have me measured. He ordered me to take off my boots so they could get the length right. The lady was in the back room for quite a long time while we sat in the salon and waited. When she returned, her arms laden with dresses of all types for every conceivable occasion, Rich sprang to his feet and began to go through them tossing me the ones he liked. Honestly, Manola, it was funny, he made up his mind in an instant, yes to this one, no to that one, just as quick as you'd leaf through magazines in search of something good to read. I went into the fitting room, and emerged, 'no' he said, 'doesn't bring out the color of your eyes,' next one, 'yes, fits perfect, we'll take it.' I gasped when I saw the price tag, but he didn't care."

"You know I've never liked black, reminds me of every funeral in the world, but Rich insisted that I try on a bunch of terribly smart *little* black dresses, and we finally settled on one that I could live with. Black satin is usually considered trampy, but this dress was so well cut, and fit me so perfectly, that I quite liked myself in it and it changed my mind about wearing black; as usual, my husband was right."

"Then the lingerie, the girls in the department fawned all over him as if I didn't exist, he loved it, the attention, the bawdy jokes, the admiration. 'I've seen it all,' said one of the older salesladies, shaking her head, 'I've been here a lot of years, Sir, but I've never seen a man shop like you before. It's really something when a man knows his lady's style, what colors she should wear, just beats me how you know her size and all.'

"He ate it up. Quite a different scene from the day when we met in Algiers and I helped him choose a robe for his mother's birthday in our Galerie de France."

She rambled on, with no regard to cost, I was glad she was phoning me, not the other way around.

"He's turned into quite the businessman, my Rich," Nadia related during another call. "He's involved in so many associations, some of which do charitable work for children, that sometimes I'm left on my own, but I've enough to do to stay busy so it's like a honeymoon all over again when he comes home. He's quite well known and well liked by the power brokers."

I wondered who they were.

"He wants to go into politics," she crowed, "imagine, me, Nadia from Algiers, being Mrs. Senator from Texas," and she guffawed, her roaring laugh still uninhibited and free.

"Did I ever tell you about that very first time I was immersed in Texas "society"? It was before the oil strike and Rich insisted I join a women's club to get acquainted. I was treated to behind-my-back comments on my appearance, "nuthin' special", my clothes, "funny", my accent, "c-u-u-u-te", my husband, "darlin'". Since then, I've tried to avoid these club ladies, but if Rich truly gets into politics, I'll have to bite the bullet, that's one American expression I've learned, and try to conform. I'll do anything for my husband, he's so thoughtful, my Rich, do you know that for my last birthday he bought me yet another prize winner — this one I plan to ride, his name is Tiger, which I know is a strange name for a horse, but it was as close as I could get to Trigger, which is Roy Roger's horse," and she bubbled on about her full life commuting between the ranch, where she preferred to be riding her horses, and town, which I gathered was Dallas, and its society.

As she meandered on through many dozens of phone calls, I formed an impression of what her life was like, and once again couldn't help comparing it to mine, her affluence and luxury, my deprivation and penury. I managed to boast about our yoga school's growing clientele of movie people, which fascinated Nadia. I explained I still had two or three other jobs, playing piano in a restaurant, hat check girl in a night club, as well as teaching French privately — all to keep a roof over my head. Nadia said she admired me for my struggles and that, sooner or later, I'd come out on top. I reflected that my early years, being raised as a spoiled child in a well-to-do home surrounded by a loving family, were now but memories, whereas Nadia, for all the squalor of her early life, was now reaping the benefits of the lucky largesse thrown to her by the hand of chance. After all, had I married Rich and not Bill, her life might have been mine, and mine hers.

"You speak better English than I do," I marveled one day during another phone call. Her precise diction and meticulous use of good vocabulary put me to shame. I was still using double negatives.

"Well, it cost enough," she replied playfully. "I had intensive tutoring because in my present position it wouldn't do to sound like a French immigrant war bride, which of course is exactly what I am." We laughed.

Now we were going to be together. She had sent me a round trip ticket to attend her husband's swearing-in as State Senator. What a proud moment for Nadia, I couldn't refuse and had scurried around to find replacements for my several responsibilities, reliable girls who were honest enough to not steal away my jobs while I was on the month-long sojourn in Texas.

Texas certainly was flat. The plane circled the Dallas airport once and touched down.

Here she came, red hair streaming behind her as usual, dressed impeccably in a well fitting expensive brown pants suit. Her jewelry was discrete, gold pin on the lapel, and matching gold earrings. Her two-tone cowboy boots and an elegant matching crocodile handbag completed her ensemble. Over the years, Nadia had grown into a true lady. I marveled at the transformation from when I'd seen her leaving the boat in Baltimore in her cheap too-tight jersey dress, her dirty camel hair coat slung, matador-style, over her shoulders.

I recognized Rich from the dock. The years had been kind to him except for his receding hair line, graying sideburns, and a slightly enlarged girth. He wore a beige western-style suit, smartly cut, a huge silver belt buckle engraved with a steer flaunting its horns, beautiful cream-colored boots and a large white Stetson which he whipped off when I approached. "Welcome to Dallas," they said in unison and we all laughed nervously. He picked up my suitcase; both hooked an arm through mine, talking all at once, they steered me to a bright red Jaguar convertible parked at the curb.

"That's my car," Nadia announced proudly, "Rich's latest gift, isn't she pretty? Rich, tell Manola what they call that color here in Texas."

He grinned down at me, "That's called *Howdy Officer Red*, I reckon you can figure out why, and this li'l gal sure do speed."

I wasn't certain he was referring to the convertible or its driver, but I was once again struck by how luck had smiled on Nadia, and agreed she was indeed pretty.

"This is Dallas, ma'am," he slowed down and indicated a modern city filled with big cars and lots of pedestrians, most wearing the ubiquitous cowboy boots. "That's standard footgear here, Manola, you have to wear boots or they think you're a foreigner, we'll get you some."

"I expected to see cowboys on horseback," I said.

"Oh you will, just wait until we get out on the range," Rich replied.

I didn't see any ten-gallon hats like in the movies, I supposed they were out of style, but many Stetsons like Rich's worn with business suits. Lots and lots of denim, checkered western shirts with pearl snap fasteners on men and women, with a stylish scarf knotted under the left ear. I looked and looked, filling my eyes with all the new and strange.

The wind whipped through my hair as we sped outside the city limits on a straight, flat road. "Slow down darling, let Manola have a look at the scenery." There really wasn't much to see other than plowed fields and herds of white-faced cattle dotting the landscape. I remarked again, this time out loud, how incredibly flat it was.

"Not like your Southern California with all its hills, I bet," Rich smiled, "this is prairie and farm land, oil rigs and cattle ranches, you'll get used to it pretty soon, I promise."

We turned off the main road at a signpost marked "Wilson" and I whistled as we approached the imposing ranch house nestled among towering trees like a jewel in its setting, framed by a circular paved drive.

"Welcome home to the Wilsons's," Nadia squeezed my arm, "nice, isn't it?"

We entered the house through an immense glass door where Rich cautioned me to watch my nose, as there was very little to indicate that a doorway existed.

She escorted me through a round foyer in the center of which was an enormous vase of fragrant flowers on an inlaid table, to the living room, which was furnished with original art, crystal chandeliers, and fine mahogany furniture. Bibelots, books, elegant carpeting, large floral arrangements in oversized jardinieres as well as silver objects were artfully arranged. My eye was caught by the bouquet in a long horizontal crystal holder which was the huge mantelpiece's only accent. The room was a gem of restraint yet opulent enough to entice the eye and relax the spirit.

"Oh Nadia," I breathed, "this is heavenly."

"It's taken years to get to this point, Manola, we had to learn about art, both of us, and collecting has become our passion, the way raising kids seems to be for other couples. We've never been able to have any, but Rich doesn't seem to mind. I decorated this room all by myself, do you truly like it?"

"It's a fairyland, really, I had no idea."

Grasping my elbow she steered me down a long hallway and threw open a door. "This is your room, the bath is just beyond, I know how much you like flowers so I hope there's enough of them," and she giggled just like the girl I remembered. There were fresh bunches, nosegays, bud vases on every surface, all welcoming and fragrant.

With the same discreet but lavish taste, this suite of rooms was decorated in old rose and brown velvet. There was one chocolate wall which led the eye to the brown-stained exposed beamed ceiling. I felt the room's greeting, and quickly unpacked my few belongings, Nadia had expressly told me to bring very little. I changed from my travel-wrinkled blouse to one from the suitcase which was a little less wrinkled.

A knock at the door revealed a smartly uniformed maid who informed me that I was expected for an aperitif. She led me back to the grand salon where I watched a tender scene unfold. Rich had just presented Nadia with a small black velvet case, and I stood in the doorway, reluctant to intrude until she had opened it. "It's to celebrate our election, darling, without your support I could never have become State Senator, I want you to wear it to the ceremony, and forever after. Never take it off."

She looked up at him wordlessly, raised the box top, and gasped, "Oh Rich, it's just gorgeous." She reached out to cover his face with kisses as he tried to clasp the chain around her neck. I felt I could go in then, and they turned to me, her eyes brimming and his tender. He had given her a good-sized diamond pendant on a platinum chain, and in the hollow of Nadia's golden throat it glimmered seductively.

It was quiet and peaceful in that room, the shadows of the tall trees swayed over the huge windows, and the heady scent of something strawberry baking tickled my nose. "Our Cecilia bakes the most delicious strawberry pies, I'm so glad strawberries are in season just now." After our drinks, we strolled down the opposite hallway in the direction of the good smells. The dining room was formal, serene and as elegant as the rest of the house, decorated with what I came to see as Nadia's individual stamp. Where had this knowledge and taste come from? I knew her poverty-stricken background, knew the underworld she sprang from; this incredible creature for all her inauspicious beginnings had turned out to have as magnificent a spirit as any lady born to the purple. Certainly she put snobbish Arlette, with all the advantages she started with, to shame.

The next days were filled with preparations for the inaugural, and, as busy as Nadia was, she took me to the famous Neiman's and insisted upon buying me a beautiful dress for the occasion, one much nicer than I could ever afford. I wore it for years, and every time I put it on its silky feel made me remember her.

"Look, don't you think this photo makes me look fat?" she demanded, shoving a folded newspaper under my nose. There, smiling, on the front page, under the headline, "Richard Wilson, new Senator from Dallas", was Rich with Nadia, also smiling, at his side. The little blurb said 'charming French wife Nadia is an expert horsewoman and gracious hostess.'"

I had a small shiver of some impending uneasiness cascade down my spine — I hadn't realized that Nadia would become a public monument, her likeness reproduced all over the state, her background and biography closely scrutinized by the press. I had a strong feeling, like the one I had on the boat, when I feared for her, what might lie in wait, being so open and accessible.

The inauguration was a blur, so many people, so many introductions, my mind was in a whirl, my face sore from smiling. There was to be a gigantic party afterward at the house, many people, old friends, new friends and constituents, neighbors and family would be in attendance and again I had the disquieting but firmly compressed sensation of something not being quite right.

I watched as Nadia poured herself another drink, raised the bottle and wordlessly invited me to join her. I shook my head and wondered if this was a usual occurrence, or merely a one-time antidote to the stress of the large number of people gathering on the lawn, and spilling into the house. Rich had the good idea to hire men to park visitors' cars and Nadia was needed to join him on an informal receiving line outside.

Her green eyes glittering, her shapely figure outlined in a dark blue silk dress, red hair piled on top into a French twist, high-heeled navy pumps completed the vision. With simple earrings and her diamond pendant, she was a study of understated elegance.

Waiters passed in and out, trays held high with filled champagne glasses. I stood back and admired the scene. The house was once again full of flowers, their heady scent added to the perfume of elegant women and the after-shave of well-groomed men. It seemed they were all talking at once, as loudly as possible in that execrable Texas accent, almost unbearable to listen to and impossible to comprehend. I overheard snatches of conversations relating to cattle, crops, politics, golf, and women's issues, the all-important clothes, babies, servants, and entertaining.

There were many envious eyes cast at Nadia and I overheard several sour remarks. "Look at her, she fell out of the sky and landed in pig heaven, how many gifts does that husband of hers give her any-way, take a look at that diamond." Another fat woman chimed in with, "I'd love to know what she eats to stay that thin, don't look too healthy though, does she?" I was glad that Nadia couldn't hear them from across the crowded room. Catty women were the same all over the world, and jealousy just fuels the flame. Nadia had not made many friends among the wives, but she was certainly popular with their men, that hadn't changed a bit. I saw her joking with one group, moving effortlessly to another, kissing an old gentleman on his ruddy cheek, laughing at another's sally — she probably didn't care a damn for the wives' opinion, any more than she had for the girls' view of her behavior on the *Bald Eagle*.

I drifted from room to room, nodding hello to some that I had already met, but not stopping to talk with anyone in particular. I had been enjoying myself, and Nadia's performance, where was she now? I ended up back in the spacious foyer just in time to experience an unpleasant feeling which had more to do with my own insecurities than what actually was occurring.

Rich had his arm around his wife, kissing the top of her hair as three ill-dressed and uneasy-look-ing men about his own age were approaching. From my vantage point behind the huge vase on the circular table, I observed that the tallest, a sandy-haired farm boy wearing a cheap suit and a wide grin, whooped as he opened his arms to encompass Rich.

"Hey boy, you sure stepped in it, din't ya?" The other two surged forward with similar exuberance leaving me to wonder what this was all about. They certainly didn't fit in here. The smaller, heavier one was wearing well-pressed denim jeans, a handsome suede jacket trimmed with fringe, and loud cowboy boots. The third one sported a grotesque tie of the type usually given at Christmas by well-meaning relatives. Who were these characters slapping Rich on the back? They looked like dressed-up farmhands. By now Rich was slapping and exclaiming, hugging them back, as Nadia stood by his side, bewildered.

"Sweetheart, when I was an M.P. in your home town, I busted these three guys more than once. I served with them, can you believe it? After all these years, imagine!"

From the back, I could see Nadia stiffen.

"This is Hank, and Pete and Vern, all good ol' boys from the State of Texas. What are you doing here anyway?"

Hank, the tall one, answered for all. "We seen yer picture in the paper down our way, did ya know we all live near each other down Dallam county by the panhandle? We know we're crashin' yer party, Rich, or should I say Mr. Senator, but we wanted ta come and say howdy, and mebbe lift a glass to yer success and good-lookin' wife." The leer that he gave Nadia was smarmy, suggestive and all-knowing. Rich never noticed, but I did.

"Oh look at my manners," Rich interjected, "this is the light of my life, say hello to my wife,

Nadia." Dutifully, like little boys at a dance being told to choose a partner, one by one, they extended their hand, mumbled some words of greeting, and looked her over out of the corner of their eyes.

I felt my anxiety rise, for what reason, I couldn't say. Nadia glanced over and saw me, "Manola, come and meet some of Rich's platoon, this is my ship-mate from Algeria, Manola."

This time they were bolder, and the tall one gave me a decided lewd wink as the little one in the suede jacket murmured something about "nice lookin' gal." I didn't know whether to be flattered or offended, but smiled neutrally, no sense letting them know what I really thought.

"Yer from North Africa too, aint'cha, Missus?" asked Pete, or was it Vern, of Nadia, a knowing smirk on his homely face.

"Yes, that's my home and that's where I met my husband," she replied, raising her chin defiantly.

"We must've met?" asked Hank with what seemed like a studied innocence, and now I knew why I had felt the sense of disquiet all day.

"No, I doubt it," Nadia brushed him off, turning to Rich.

"Darling, perhaps these gentlemen," and she put a heavy stress on the word, "would like a drink, I'm sure they're thirsty after their long drive."

"Come on in the bar, boys, it's open and there's plenty for all," Rich laughed, leading the way, threading through the well-wishers, stopping to shake hands. I linked arms with Nadia and whispered, "what's wrong, do you know them?"

"Do I? Manola, what are the chances that in all of this enormous state of Texas the very three servicemen who could do me the worst harm are here under my husband's roof tonight posing as friends?"

"They seem not to be his type," I said.

"They're not, believe me. I didn't know the difference either when we were all getting acquainted with the American G.I.s." and she snorted on the word acquainted. I flashed back to our shipboard confessions and stopped in my tracks.

"You're not going to tell me that you ..."

"All of them," she replied looking me straight in the eye, "all of them except Rich, of course."

"Oh, Nadia" I moaned, "what rotten luck. I think they recognized you, what are you going to do?"

"Stop their innuendoes before Rich cottons on, and curtail the booze so their lips don't flap, and get them out of here quickly before they can do any damage."

We opened the door to the bar and entered. Except for the three yokels on their stools, and Rich behind, pouring, the room was empty. Each man tried to out-talk the next, oblivious of his neighbor.

"Here you are, do you girls want to carry on with the champagne or do you want a *real* drink?" teased Rich waving a bottle of bourbon.

"Make me a double," said Nadia, "but dear, may I please take you away from your friends for just a moment, I have to tell you something important."

Rich and Nadia left the room to the hootings of the three men who turned on me.

"So, missus, did ya marry yerself a G.I. too?" asked the little rat-faced Vern as I approached.

"Yes, I did," I replied.

"All you French gals look real nice," philosophized Pete into his near-empty glass. I wasn't sure whether to try to play surrogate hostess, but discretion won out; if he got drunk, ugly things might emerge and I didn't want to be responsible.

Nadia came back alone. "Rich has to take photographs, and I will have to join him soon, but I did want to thank you for coming, gentlemen," and she lifted her glass in a most dismissive manner, knocking back her drink.

"Hey, jes' hol' on there a moment, li'l lady, we've got some business to discuss," and Hank swung his lanky frame around to confront Nadia eye to eye.

"Business, what business?" she demanded, her tone haughty in her best Lady Bountiful manner.

"Me an' the boys here, we think you an' us'ns are ol' cronies. The reason we're here today, ain't jes' to fawn all over yer ol' man, but to see you face to face an' be sure yer the same gal we all knew so well in Algiers."

Nadia's face went white.

"As it happens, missus, you lucked out, from streetwalker scrounging meals off G.I.s an' payin' the ol'-fashion' way," and he snickered, "to great lady, wife of a Senator — you really made out good, whereas we, who fought like devils an' got hurt for our lousy pay, we *still* got nuthin'. Vern here works as a fry-cook on 'counta his disability, and Pete's a garage mechanic. I'm a hardscrabble farmer same as my ol' man, in short lady, we got nuthin' and you got everythin'."

I was impressed by Nadia's composure and tensely waited for the fireworks to explode.

Vern continued, "Somehow that don't seem fair to the boys an' me, and seein' as how Senator Rich don't know nuthin' about your shady past, an' him havin' a reputation to keep up as Senator an' all, we figger you should kinda even things up a bit, and shake loose with some long green to keep us quiet-like," and he dropped his voice to an insinuat-ing purr.

Because the door was closed, even though we could hear people in the hallway, no one came in to rescue Nadia.

I held my breath, what was she going to respond?

Whether to buy time or what, Nadia smiled, went behind the bar, topped off everyone's drinks, and poured herself another double. She raised her glass and, looking at each man in turn, said, "Gentlemen, you must be joking. You have me con-fused with someone else, and besides, even if what you accuse me of is true, do you honestly think my own husband wouldn't know?"

That was a good bluff, Nadia, let's see if they buy it.

She tossed her drink back again like a profes-sional and Pete crowed, "that's her, that's her all right, that gal sure could drink, jes' like you."

"That's a mighty nice diamond," commented Hank, leaning over the bar to get a better look, "we could consider that a first installment on that there debt we was talkin' about."

"The paper said you was an expert horse-woman," added Pete, "mebbe ya got some good horseflesh fer a second installment."

"Yeah, and look at this house," Vern chipped in, "don't tell me ya can't raise some money with all the good stuff ya got here?" He reached out and pat-ted a large bronze sculpture of a horse rearing at the sight of a rattlesnake beneath its hooves. The body of the rider, poised, balanced just so, indicated a very fine piece of work I was sure I had seen in a museum.

"I'm not giving you anything," Nadia laughed, "look at you, bunch of losers, do you honestly think my husband is going to listen to anything the likes of you have to say? Of course not, you can't tell him anything he doesn't already know from me, so forgive me for bein' ornery, boys, but no deal." To punctuate her statement, she threw back her hair and laughed right in their faces, which made them angry. Tempers and voices began to rise. She slammed her empty glass down on the bar, and, pointing to the door, raised her voice, "get out of my house."

"We ain't goin' nowhere until we talk to Rich, right boys?" asked Hank in a wavering tone as the other two looked away and didn't meet his eyes. Was it possible she had bluffed them and they really had no intention of telling their story to her husband?

Storming to the door, albeit a little unsteadily, she flung it open saying loudly, "you're not welcome here, please leave, or I will." No one moved. She looked directly at me, shrugged and strode out, banging the door closed. I ran after her.

"Nadia, what are you doing?"

"Go find Rich, Manola, tell him to make some excuse for me, that I'm not feeling well, dinner will just have to be delayed until we get rid of some of the trash. Not all the guests are staying, only the important ones, but I've got to be alone to think how I'm going to work this out. I don't believe they'll tell Rich anything as long as I'm not here. Go on, it's all right, I'll see you later."

"I'll go with you," I offered.

"No, no, you'll just be in the way, please, do as I ask you, don't worry, and for God's sake, go inside, I don't want you to catch your death of a cold." She smiled tenderly, blew me a kiss, and swept off to go, where, I didn't know. But I did worry. I stood outside the door, wishing I had insisted she take me with her on her soul-searching mission. It was starting to get dark, I hesitated to go in, my task undone.

Rich had drunk rather more than was good for him, he was plainly worried, pacing and non-communicative, even to his three army buddies who whispered among themselves, not looking in my direction. Rich knew his wife had taken the car, I had told him how much she had to drink and the furrows in his forehead deepened even more.

It wasn't much later with the invited dinner guests, hungry and whispering about the hostess's unexplained absence, when the troopers came.

"Sorry to interrupt your celebration, Senator Wilson, but can we talk privately?" asked one grave-faced policeman.

He emerged from the library with the two officers, his face a gray mask of emptiness and shock.

"Manola, please, come with me. They found her, wrapped around a tree not far away. She totaled the car taking the curve too fast."

I gasped. "She's not...?" I couldn't say the word out loud. If I did, it would become true.

He started to crumble then, sobs racking his big form, leaning on me for support which I could hardly give, I was so shattered myself.

They drove us to the scene. She must have been going very, very fast as the beautiful red car and its even more beautiful red-haired occupant were indistinguishable from twisted metal, blood, broken glass and broken body, thorny branches from the tree she collided with. As the Jaguar was a convertible she was thrown free, landing with her neck twisted at an odd angle, the diamond pendant, its brilliance dimmed by the dust pressing against her cheek, the same dust that was slowly soaking up the blood that flowed from her ear, nose, and mouth.

"From dust we come and to dust we return," I whispered to no one in particular. I would always remember her vibrant laugh sliding up the scale, the demonstrative gestures of her slender hands, the scent of her heady perfume.

"She died instantly, Sir," the officer said. "I'm sure she never knew what hit her — or rather, what she hit."

Rich sobbed out loud, moaning like an injured animal in his pain. There was nothing I could add, say, or do to comfort him, I was numb as someone dead, as dead as she was.

They drove us back to the house and it fell to me to send the dinner guests home; I had to pull myself together to relate the sad story, and had to remain strong. Rich was in no state to speak to anyone, the three army buddies filed out without looking at me, their eyes cast down, along with their hopes.

At least her secret never came out, Rich was secure in his memory of her, but for me, I still cringe at the sound of that back-country accent when I chance upon it, because I know they were responsible for her unnecessary and premature death.

Poor Nadia, she had the best chance at success in her marriage, but if she had lived, who knows? Perhaps conditions might have changed, and there would not have been so idyllic a future for her — now no one would ever know.

EPILOGUE

Somewhere in the vastness of the ocean, obscure echo of a time long past, a bottle bobs along with its precious contents. It has harbored so much fear. It has fought many brutal battles against foaming, choleric waves, which broke down on it with ferocity. Sometimes it bounced along happily under a starry canopy in the cloudless night, and, listening to the water's rising murmurs, it hoped for silted sands and idle lands to rest upon.

Time has passed when, aboard a ship, seven little notes, portions of hopes, fears, even regrets, were scribbled by seven young women who wished to perpetuate their memories, their adventures, and hoped that someday, somewhere, someone would find the bottle and thus forever keep the dreams alive.

It was their way to bring to the future the secrets of their souls, the sum total of their expected visions — after all, there would be no life without dreams. Destiny sees it otherwise; for some of us the expectations came true, others witnessed their death, and one or two were active in their own destruction.

Should the magic bottle crack open, and, like white butterflies the little papers escape, only to be swallowed up by the unalterable ocean and disappear, it would keep their secrets and give them an honorable resting place. Should the currents roll the bottle ashore and some stranger stumble upon it, and with trembling fingers shatter the glass and read the words, please consider from whom they come, and respect them for what they are.

ORDER FORM

Please send me _____ copies of the book
BOTTLED DREAMS.

PRICE PER BOOK ....$24.95 each
Shipping and Handling (per book) ....$ 4.00 each
(Note: California residents add 7.75% sales tax)

Ship to:

_____
(Full name)

_____
(Street address)

_____
(City)   (State)   (Zip Code)

Mail to:
Abbott/Adele Books   (Amount enclosed$_____)
P.O. Box 10281
Napa, CA 94581

☐ Please send me information about other books by
     Monette Goetinck.